Counting Techniques, Probability, and the Binomial Theorem

Jerome E. Kaufmann | Karen L. Schwitters

Australia • Brazil • Japan • Korea • Mexico • Singapore • Spain • United Kingdom • United States

Counting Techniques, Probability, and the Binomial Theorem

Algebra for College Students, 8th Edition
Jerome E. Kaufmann | Karen L. Schwitters

Executive Editors:
Maureen Staudt
Michael Stranz

Senior Project Development Manager:
Linda deStefano

Marketing Specialist:
Courtney Sheldon

Senior Production/Manufacturing Manager:
Donna M. Brown

PreMedia Manager:
Joel Brennecke

Sr. Rights Acquisition Account Manager:
Todd Osborne

Cover Image:
Getty Images*

*Unless otherwise noted, all cover images used by Custom Solutions, a part of Cengage Learning, have been supplied courtesy of Getty Images with the exception of the Earthview cover image, which has been supplied by the National Aeronautics and Space Administration (NASA).

ISBN-13: 978-1-111-46683-1

ISBN-10: 1-111-46683-1

Cengage Learning
5191 Natorp Boulevard
Mason, Ohio 45040
USA

Cengage Learning is a leading provider of customized learning solutions with office locations around the globe, including Singapore, the United Kingdom, Australia, Mexico, Brazil, and Japan. Locate your local office at:
international.cengage.com/region.

Cengage Learning products are represented in Canada by Nelson Education, Ltd.
For your lifelong learning solutions, visit **www.cengage.com /custom.**
Visit our corporate website at **www.cengage.com.**

Printed in the United States of America

15

Counting Techniques, Probability, and the Binomial Theorem

Probability theory can determine the probability of winning a game of chance such as a lottery.

In a group of 30 people, there is approximately a 70% chance that at least 2 of them will have the same birthday (same month and same day of the month). In a group of 60 people, there is approximately a 99% chance that at least 2 of them will have the same birthday.

With an ordinary deck of 52 playing cards, there is 1 chance out of 54,145 that you will be dealt four aces in a five-card hand. The radio is predicting a 40% chance of locally severe thunderstorms by late afternoon. The odds in favor of the Cubs winning the pennant are 2 to 3. Suppose that in a box containing 50 light bulbs, 45 are good ones, and 5 are burned out. If 2 bulbs are chosen at random, the probability of getting at least 1 good bulb is $\frac{243}{245}$. Historically, many basic probability concepts have been developed as a result of studying various games of chance. However, in recent years, applications of probability have been surfacing at a phenomenal rate in a large variety of fields, such as physics, biology, psychology, economics, insurance, military science, manufacturing, and politics. It is our purpose in this chapter first to introduce some counting techniques and then to use those techniques to explore some basic concepts of probability. The last section of the chapter will be devoted to the binomial theorem.

15.1 Fundamental Principle of Counting

One very useful counting principle is referred to as the **fundamental principle of counting**. We will offer some examples, state the property, and then use it to solve a variety of counting problems. Let's consider two problems to lead up to the statement of the property.

PROBLEM 1

A woman has four skirts and five blouses. Assuming that each blouse can be worn with each skirt, how many different skirt–blouse outfits does she have?

Solution

For *each* of the four skirts, she has a choice of five blouses. Therefore she has $4(5) = 20$ different skirt–blouse outfits from which to choose. ■

PROBLEM 2

Eric is shopping for a new bicycle and has two different models (5-speed or 10-speed) and four different colors (red, white, blue, or silver) from which to choose. How many different choices does he have?

Solution

His different choices can be counted with the help of a **tree diagram**.

Models	Colors	Choices
5-speed	red	5-speed red
	white	5-speed white
	blue	5-speed blue
	silver	5-speed silver
10-speed	red	10-speed red
	white	10-speed white
	blue	10-speed blue
	silver	10-speed silver

For each of the two model choices, there are four choices of color. Altogether, then, Eric has $2(4) = 8$ choices. ■

These two problems exemplify the following general principle:

Fundamental Principle of Counting

If one task can be accomplished in x different ways and, following this task, a second task can be accomplished in y different ways, then the first task followed by the second task can be accomplished in $x \cdot y$ different ways. (This counting principle can be extended to any finite number of tasks.)

As you apply the fundamental principle of counting, it is often helpful to analyze a problem systematically in terms of the tasks to be accomplished. Let's consider some examples.

PROBLEM 3

How many numbers of three different digits each can be formed by choosing from the digits 1, 2, 3, 4, 5 and 6?

Solution

Let's analyze this problem in terms of three tasks.

Task 1 Choose the hundreds digit, for which there are six choices.

Task 2 Now choose the tens digit, for which there are only five choices because one digit was used in the hundreds place.

Task 3 Now choose the units digit, for which there are only four choices because two digits have been used for the other places.

Therefore task 1 followed by task 2 followed by task 3 can be accomplished in $(6)(5)(4) = 120$ ways. In other words, there are 120 numbers of three different digits that can be formed by choosing from the six given digits. ■

Now look back over the solution for Problem 3 and think about each of the following questions:

1. Can we solve the problem by choosing the units digit first, then the tens digit, and finally the hundreds digit?
2. How many three-digit numbers can be formed from 1, 2, 3, 4, 5, and 6 if we do not require each number to have three *different* digits? (Your answer should be 216.)
3. Suppose that the digits from which to choose are 0, 1, 2, 3, 4, and 5. Now how many numbers of three different digits each can be formed, assuming that we do not want zero in the hundreds place? (Your answer should be 100.)
4. Suppose that we want to know the number of *even* numbers with three different digits each that can be formed by choosing from 1, 2, 3, 4, 5, and 6. How many are there? (Your answer should be 60.)

PROBLEM 4

Employee ID numbers at a certain factory consist of one capital letter followed by a three-digit number that contains no repeat digits. For example, A-014 is an ID number. How many such ID numbers can be formed? How many can be formed if repeated digits *are* allowed?

Solution

Again, let's analyze the problem in terms of tasks to be completed.

Task 1 Choose the letter part of the ID number: there are 26 choices.

Task 2 Choose the first digit of the three-digit number: there are ten choices.

Task 3 Choose the second digit: there are nine choices.

Task 4 Choose the third digit: there are eight choices.

Therefore, applying the fundamental principle, we obtain $(26)(10)(9)(8) = 18{,}720$ possible ID numbers.

If repeat digits were allowed, then there would be $(26)(10)(10)(10) = 26{,}000$ possible ID numbers. ■

PROBLEM 5

In how many ways can Al, Barb, Chad, Dan, and Edna be seated in a row of five seats so that Al and Barb are seated side by side?

Solution

This problem can be analyzed in terms of three tasks.

Task 1 Choose the two adjacent seats to be occupied by Al and Barb. An illustration such as Figure 15.1 helps us to see that there are four choices for the two adjacent seats.

Figure 15.1

Task 2 Determine the number of ways in which Al and Barb can be seated. Because Al can be seated on the left and Barb on the right, or vice versa, there are two ways to seat Al and Barb for each pair of adjacent seats.

Task 3 The remaining three people must be seated in the remaining three seats. This can be done in $(3)(2)(1) = 6$ different ways.

Therefore, by the fundamental principle, task 1 followed by task 2 followed by task 3 can be done in $(4)(2)(6) = 48$ ways. ■

Suppose that in Problem 5, we wanted instead the number of ways in which the five people can sit so that Al and Barb are *not* side by side. We can determine this number by using either of two basically different techniques: (1) analyze and count the number of nonadjacent positions for Al and Barb, or (2) subtract the number of seating arrangements determined in Problem 5 from the total number of ways in which five people can be seated in five seats. Try doing this problem both ways, and see whether you agree with the answer of 72 ways.

As you apply the fundamental principle of counting, you may find that for certain problems, simply thinking about an appropriate tree diagram is helpful, even though the size of the problem may make it inappropriate to write out the diagram in detail. Consider the following problem.

PROBLEM 6

Suppose that the undergraduate students in three departments — geography, history, and psychology — are to be classified according to sex and year in school. How many categories are needed?

Solution

Let's represent the various classifications symbolically as follows:

M:	Male	1.	Freshman	G:	Geography
F:	Female	2.	Sophomore	H:	History
		3.	Junior	P:	Psychology
		4.	Senior		

We can mentally picture a tree diagram such that each of the two sex classifications branches into four school-year classifications, which in turn branch into three department classifications. Thus we have $(2)(4)(3) = 24$ different categories. ■

Another technique that works on certain problems involves what some people call the *back door* approach. For example, suppose we know that the classroom contains 50 seats. On some days, it may be easier to determine the number of students present by counting the number of empty seats and subtracting from 50 than by counting the number of students in attendance. (We suggested this back door approach as one way to count the nonadjacent seating arrangements in the discussion following Problem 5.) The next example further illustrates this approach.

PROBLEM 7

When rolling a pair of dice, in how many ways can we obtain a sum greater than 4?

Solution

For clarification purposes, let's use a red die and a white die. (It is not necessary to use different-colored dice, but it does help us analyze the different possible outcomes.) With a moment of thought, you will see that there are more ways to get a sum greater than 4 than there are ways to get a sum of 4 or less. Therefore let's determine the number of possibilities for getting a sum of 4 or less; then we'll subtract that number from the total number of possible outcomes when rolling a pair of dice. First, we can simply list and count the ways of getting a sum of 4 or less.

Red die	White die
1	1
1	2
1	3
2	1
2	2
3	1

There are six ways of getting a sum of 4 or less.

Second, because there are six possible outcomes on the red die and six possible outcomes on the white die, there is a total of $(6)(6) = 36$ possible outcomes when rolling a pair of dice.

Therefore, subtracting the number of ways of getting 4 or less from the total number of possible outcomes, we obtain $36 - 6 = 30$ ways of getting a sum greater than 4. ■

Problem Set 15.1

Solve Problems 1–37.

1. If a woman has two skirts and ten blouses, how many different skirt–blouse combinations does she have?

2. If a man has eight shirts, five pairs of slacks, and three pairs of shoes, how many different shirt–slacks–shoe combinations does he have?

3. In how many ways can four people be seated in a row of four seats?

4. How many numbers of two different digits can be formed by choosing from the digits 1, 2, 3, 4, 5, 6, and 7?

5. How many *even* numbers of three different digits can be formed by choosing from the digits 2, 3, 4, 5, 6, 7, 8, and 9?

6. How many *odd* numbers of four different digits can be formed by choosing from the digits 1, 2, 3, 4, 5, 6, 7, and 8?

7. Suppose that the students at a certain university are to be classified according to their college (College of Applied Science, College of Arts and Sciences, College of Business, College of Education, College of Fine Arts, College of Health and Physical Education), sex (female, male), and year in school (1, 2, 3, 4). How many categories are possible?

8. A medical researcher classifies subjects according to sex (female, male), smoking habits (smoker, nonsmoker), and weight (below average, average, above average). How many different combined classifications are used?

9. A pollster classifies voters according to sex (female, male), party affiliation (Democrat, Republican, Independent), and family income (below $10,000, $10,000–$19,999, $20,000–$29,999, $30,000–$39,999, $40,000–$49,999, $50,000 and above). How many combined classifications does the pollster use?

10. A couple is planning to have four children. How many ways can this happen in terms of boy–girl classification? (For example, *BBBG* indicates that the first three children are boys and the last is a girl.)

11. In how many ways can three officers — president, secretary, and treasurer — be selected from a club that has 20 members?

12. In how many ways can three officers — president, secretary, and treasurer — be selected from a club with 15 female and 10 male members so that the president is female and the secretary and treasurer are male?

13. A disc jockey wants to play six songs once each in a half-hour program. How many different ways can he order these songs?

14. A state has agreed to have its automobile license plates consist of two letters followed by four digits. State officials do not want to repeat any letters or digits in any license numbers. How many different license plates will be available?

15. In how many ways can six people be seated in a row of six seats?

16. In how many ways can Al, Bob, Carlos, Don, Ed, and Fern be seated in a row of six seats if Al and Bob want to sit side by side?

17. In how many ways can Amy, Bob, Cindy, Dan, and Elmer be seated in a row of five seats so that neither Amy nor Bob occupies an end seat?

18. In how many ways can Al, Bob, Carlos, Don, Ed, and Fern be seated in a row of six seats if Al and Bob are not to be seated side by side? [*Hint*: Either Al and Bob will be seated side by side or they will not be seated side by side.]

19. In how many ways can Al, Bob, Carol, Dawn, and Ed be seated in a row of five chairs if Al is to be seated in the middle chair?

20. In how many ways can three letters be dropped in five mailboxes?

21. In how many ways can five letters be dropped in three mailboxes?

22. In how many ways can four letters be dropped in six mailboxes so that no two letters go in the same box?

23. In how many ways can six letters be dropped in four mailboxes so that no two letters go in the same box?

24. If five coins are tossed, in how many ways can they fall?

25. If three dice are tossed, in how many ways can they fall?

26. In how many ways can a sum less than ten be obtained when tossing a pair of dice?

27. In how many ways can a sum greater than five be obtained when tossing a pair of dice?

28. In how many ways can a sum greater than four be obtained when tossing three dice?

29. If no number contains repeated digits, how many numbers greater than 400 can be formed by choosing from the digits 2, 3, 4, and 5? [*Hint*: Consider both three-digit and four-digit numbers.]

30. If no number contains repeated digits, how many numbers greater than 5000 can be formed by choosing from the digits 1, 2, 3, 4, 5, and 6?

31. In how many ways can four boys and three girls be seated in a row of seven seats so that boys and girls occupy alternating seats?

32. In how many ways can three different mathematics books and four different history books be exhibited on a shelf so that all of the books in a subject area are side by side?

33. In how many ways can a true–false test of ten questions be answered?

34. If no number contains repeated digits, how many even numbers greater than 3000 can be formed by choosing from the digits 1, 2, 3, and 4?

35. If no number contains repeated digits, how many odd numbers greater than 40,000 can be formed by choosing from the digits 1, 2, 3, 4, and 5?

36. In how many ways can Al, Bob, Carol, Don, Ed, Faye, and George be seated in a row of seven seats so that Al, Bob, and Carol occupy consecutive seats in some order?

37. The license plates for a certain state consist of two letters followed by a four-digit number such that the first digit of the number is not zero. An example is PK-2446.

(a) How many different license plates can be produced?

(b) How many different plates do not have a repeated letter?

(c) How many plates do not have any repeated digits in the number part of the plate?

(d) How many plates do not have a repeated letter and also do not have any repeated digits?

THOUGHTS INTO WORDS

38. How would you explain the fundamental principle of counting to a friend who missed class the day it was discussed?

39. Give two or three simple illustrations of the fundamental principle of counting.

40. Explain how you solved Problem 29.

15.2 Permutations and Combinations

As we develop the material in this section, **factorial notation** becomes very useful. The notation $n!$ (which is read "n factorial") is used with positive integers as follows:

$$1! = 1$$

$$2! = 2 \cdot 1 = 2$$

$$3! = 3 \cdot 2 \cdot 1 = 6$$

$$4! = 4 \cdot 3 \cdot 2 \cdot 1 = 24$$

Note that the factorial notation refers to an *indicated product*. In general, we write

$$n! = n(n-1)(n-2) \cdot \cdot \cdot 3 \cdot 2 \cdot 1$$

We also define $0! = 1$ so that certain formulas will be true for all nonnegative integers.

Now, as an introduction to the first concept of this section, let's consider a counting problem that closely resembles problems from the previous section.

PROBLEM 1

In how many ways can the three letters A, B, and C be arranged in a row?

Solution A

Certainly one approach to the problem is simply to list and count the arrangements.

ABC ACB BAC BCA CAB CBA

There are six arrangements of the three letters.

Solution B

Another approach, one that can be generalized for more difficult problems, uses the fundamental principle of counting. Because there are three choices for the first letter of an arrangement, two choices for the second letter, and one choice for the third letter, there are $(3)(2)(1) = 6$ arrangements. ■

Permutations

Ordered arrangements are called **permutations**. In general, a permutation of a set of n elements is an ordered arrangement of the n elements; we will use the symbol $P(n, n)$ to denote the number of such permutations. For example, from Problem 1, we know that $P(3, 3) = 6$. Furthermore, by using the same basic approach as in Solution B of Problem 1, we can obtain

$$P(1, 1) = 1 = 1!$$

$$P(2, 2) = 2 \cdot 1 = 2!$$

$$P(4, 4) = 4 \cdot 3 \cdot 2 \cdot 1 = 4!$$

$$P(5, 5) = 5 \cdot 4 \cdot 3 \cdot 2 \cdot 1 = 5!$$

In general, the following formula becomes evident:

$$P(n, n) = n!$$

Now suppose that we are interested in the number of two-letter permutations that can be formed by choosing from the four letters A, B, C, and D. (Some examples of such permutations are AB, BA, AC, BC, and CB.) In other words, we want to find the number of two-element permutations that can be formed from a set of four elements. We denote this number by $P(4, 2)$. To find $P(4, 2)$, we can reason as follows. First, we can choose any one of the four letters to occupy the first position in the permutation, and then we can choose any one of the three remaining letters for the second position. Therefore, by the fundamental principle of counting, we have $(4)(3) = 12$ different two-letter permutations; that is, $P(4, 2) = 12$. By using a similar line of reasoning, we can determine the following numbers. (Make sure that you agree with each of these.)

$$P(4, 3) = 4 \cdot 3 \cdot 2 = 24$$

$$P(5, 2) = 5 \cdot 4 = 20$$

$$P(6, 4) = 6 \cdot 5 \cdot 4 \cdot 3 = 360$$

$$P(7, 3) = 7 \cdot 6 \cdot 5 = 210$$

In general, we say that the number of r-element permutations that can be formed from a set of n elements is given by

$$P(n, r) = \underbrace{n(n-1)(n-2)\cdots}_{r \text{ factors}}$$

Note that the indicated product for $P(n, r)$ begins with n. Thereafter, each factor is 1 less than the previous one, and there is a total of r factors. For example,

$$P(6, 2) = 6 \cdot 5 = 30$$

$$P(8, 3) = 8 \cdot 7 \cdot 6 = 336$$

$$P(9, 4) = 9 \cdot 8 \cdot 7 \cdot 6 = 3024$$

Let's consider two problems that illustrate the use of $P(n, n)$ and $P(n, r)$.

PROBLEM 2

In how many ways can five students be seated in a row of five seats?

Solution

The problem is asking for the number of five-element permutations that can be formed from a set of five elements. Thus we can apply $P(n, n) = n!$.

$$P(5, 5) = 5! = 5 \cdot 4 \cdot 3 \cdot 2 \cdot 1 = 120$$

■

PROBLEM 3

Suppose that seven people enter a swimming race. In how many ways can first, second, and third prizes be awarded?

Solution

This problem is asking for the number of three-element permutations that can be formed from a set of seven elements. Therefore, using the formula for $P(n, r)$, we obtain

$$P(7, 3) = 7 \cdot 6 \cdot 5 = 210$$

■

It should be evident that both Problem 2 and Problem 3 could have been solved by applying the fundamental principle of counting. In fact, the formulas for $P(n, n)$ and $P(n, r)$ do not really give us much additional problem-solving power. However, as we will see in a moment, they do provide the basis for developing a formula that is very useful as a problem-solving tool.

Permutations Involving Nondistinguishable Objects

Suppose we have two identical H's and one T in an arrangement such as HTH. If we switch the two identical H's, the newly formed arrangement, HTH, will not be distinguishable from the original. In other words, there are fewer distinguishable permutations of n elements when some of those elements are identical than when the n elements are distinctly different.

To see the effect of identical elements on the number of distinguishable permutations, let's look at some specific examples:

2 identical H's	1 permutation (HH)
2 different letters	2! permutations (HT, TH)

Therefore, having two different letters affects the number of permutations by a *factor of* 2!.

3 identical H's	1 permutation (HHH)
3 different letters	3! permutations

Therefore, having three different letters affects the number of permutations by a *factor of* 3!.

4 identical H's	1 permutation (HHHH)
4 different letters	4! permutations

Therefore, having four different letters affects the number of permutations by a *factor of* 4!.

Now let's solve a specific problem.

PROBLEM 4

How many distinguishable permutations can be formed from three identical H's and two identical T's?

Solution

If we had five distinctly different letters, we could form 5! permutations. But the three identical H's affect the number of distinguishable permutations by a factor of 3!, and the two identical T's affect the number of permutations by a factor of 2!. Therefore we must divide 5! by 3! and 2!. We obtain

$$\frac{5!}{(3!)(2!)} = \frac{5 \cdot \overset{2}{\cancel{4}} \cdot \cancel{3} \cdot 2 \cdot 1}{\cancel{3} \cdot 2 \cdot 1 \cdot 2 \cdot 1} = 10$$

distinguishable permutations of three H's and two T's. ■

The type of reasoning used in Problem 4 leads us to the following general counting technique. If there are n elements to be arranged, where there are r_1 of one kind, r_2 of another kind, r_3 of another kind, . . . , r_k of a kth kind, then the total number of distinguishable permutations is given by the expression

$$\frac{n!}{(r_1!)(r_2!)(r_3!) \cdots (r_k!)}$$

PROBLEM 5

How many different 11-letter permutations can be formed from the 11 letters of the word MISSISSIPPI?

Solution

Because there are 4 I's, 4 S's, and 2 P's, we can form

$$\frac{11!}{(4!)(4!)(2!)} = \frac{11 \cdot 10 \cdot 9 \cdot 8 \cdot 7 \cdot 6 \cdot 5 \cdot 4 \cdot 3 \cdot 2 \cdot 1}{4 \cdot 3 \cdot 2 \cdot 1 \cdot 4 \cdot 3 \cdot 2 \cdot 1 \cdot 2 \cdot 1} = 34{,}650$$

distinguishable permutations. ■

Combinations (Subsets)

Permutations are *ordered* arrangements; however, *order* is often not a consideration. For example, suppose that we want to determine the number of three-person committees that can be formed from the five people Al, Barb, Carol, Dawn, and Eric. Certainly the committee consisting of Al, Barb, and Eric is the same as the committee consisting of Barb, Eric, and Al. In other words, the order in which we choose or list the members is not important. Therefore we are really dealing with subsets; that is, we are looking for the number of three-element subsets that can be formed from a set of five elements. Traditionally in this context, subsets have been called **combinations**. Stated another way, then, we are looking for the number of combinations of five things taken three at a time. In general, r-element subsets taken from a set of n elements are called **combinations of n things taken r at a time**. The symbol $C(n, r)$ denotes the number of these combinations.

Now let's restate that committee problem and show a detailed solution that can be generalized to handle a variety of problems dealing with combinations.

PROBLEM 6

How many three-person committees can be formed from the five people Al, Barb, Carol, Dawn, and Eric?

Solution

Let's use the set {A, B, C, D, E} to represent the five people. Consider one possible three-person committee (subset), such as {A, B, C}; there are 3! permutations of these three letters. Now take another committee, such as {A, B, D}; there are also 3! permutations of these three letters. If we were to continue this process with all of the three-letter subsets that can be formed from the five letters, we would be counting all possible three-letter permutations of the five letters. That is, we would obtain $P(5, 3)$. Therefore, if we let $C(5, 3)$ represent the number of three-element subsets, then

$$(3!) \cdot C(5, 3) = P(5, 3)$$

Solving this equation for $C(5, 3)$ yields

$$C(5, 3) = \frac{P(5, 3)}{3!} = \frac{5 \cdot 4 \cdot 3}{3 \cdot 2 \cdot 1} = 10$$

Thus ten three-person committees can be formed from the five people. ■

In general, $C(n, r)$ times $r!$ yields $P(n, r)$. Thus

$$(r!) \cdot C(n, r) = P(n, r)$$

and solving this equation for $C(n, r)$ produces

$$C(n, r) = \frac{P(n, r)}{r!}$$

In other words, we can find the number of *combinations* of n things taken r at a time by dividing by $r!$, the number of permutations of n things taken r at a time. The following examples illustrate this idea:

$$C(7, 3) = \frac{P(7, 3)}{3!} = \frac{7 \cdot 6 \cdot 5}{3 \cdot 2 \cdot 1} = 35$$

$$C(9, 2) = \frac{P(9, 2)}{2!} = \frac{9 \cdot 8}{2 \cdot 1} = 36$$

$$C(10, 4) = \frac{P(10, 4)}{4!} = \frac{10 \cdot 9 \cdot 8 \cdot 7}{4 \cdot 3 \cdot 2 \cdot 1} = 210$$

PROBLEM 7

How many different five-card hands can be dealt from a deck of 52 playing cards?

Solution

Because the order in which the cards are dealt is not an issue, we are working with a combination (subset) problem. Thus, using the formula for $C(n, r)$, we obtain

$$C(52, 5) = \frac{P(52, 5)}{5!} = \frac{52 \cdot 51 \cdot 50 \cdot 49 \cdot 48}{5 \cdot 4 \cdot 3 \cdot 2 \cdot 1} = 2{,}598{,}960$$

There are 2,598,960 different five-card hands that can be dealt from a deck of 52 playing cards. ■

Some counting problems, such as Problem 8, can be solved by using the fundamental principle of counting along with the combination formula.

PROBLEM 8

How many committees that consist of three women and two men can be formed from a group of five women and four men?

Solution

Let's think of this problem in terms of two tasks.

Task 1 Choose a subset of three women from the five women. This can be done in

$$C(5, 3) = \frac{P(5, 3)}{3!} = \frac{5 \cdot 4 \cdot 3}{3 \cdot 2 \cdot 1} = 10 \text{ ways}$$

Task 2 Choose a subset of two men from the four men. This can be done in

$$C(4, 2) = \frac{P(4, 2)}{2!} = \frac{4 \cdot 3}{2 \cdot 1} = 6 \text{ ways}$$

Task 1 followed by task 2 can be done in $(10)(6) = 60$ ways. Therefore there are 60 committees consisting of three women and two men that can be formed. ■

Sometimes it takes a little thought to decide whether permutations or combinations should be used. Remember that **if order is to be considered, permutations should be used, but if order does not matter, then use combinations**. It is helpful to think of combinations as subsets.

PROBLEM 9

A small accounting firm has 12 computer programmers. Three of these people are to be promoted to systems analysts. In how many ways can the firm select the three people to be promoted?

Solution

Let's call the people A, B, C, D, E, F, G, H, I, J, K, and L. Suppose A, B, and C are chosen for promotion. Is this any different from choosing B, C, and A? Obviously not, so order does not matter, and we are being asked a question about combinations. More specifically, we need to find the number of combinations of 12 people taken three at a time. Thus there are

$$C(12, 3) = \frac{P(12, 3)}{3!} = \frac{12 \cdot 11 \cdot 10}{3 \cdot 2 \cdot 1} = 220$$

different ways to choose the three people to be promoted. ■

PROBLEM 10

A club is to elect three officers — president, secretary, and treasurer — from a group of six people, all of whom are willing to serve in any office. How many different ways can the officers be chosen?

Solution

Let's call the candidates A, B, C, D, E, and F. Is electing A as president, B as secretary, and C as treasurer different from electing B as president, C as secretary, and A as treasurer? Obviously it is, so we are working with permutations. Thus there are

$$P(6, 3) = 6 \cdot 5 \cdot 4 = 120$$

different ways of filling the offices. ■

Problem Set 15.2

In Problems 1–12, evaluate each.

1. $P(5, 3)$

2. $P(8, 2)$

3. $P(6, 4)$

4. $P(9, 3)$

5. $C(7, 2)$

6. $C(8, 5)$

7. $C(10, 5)$

8. $C(12, 4)$

9. $C(15, 2)$

10. $P(5, 5)$

11. $C(5, 5)$

12. $C(11, 1)$

For Problems 13–44, solve each problem.

13. How many permutations of the four letters A, B, C, and D can be formed by using all the letters in each permutation?

14. In how many ways can six students be seated in a row of six seats?

15. How many three-person committees can be formed from a group of nine people?

16. How many two-card hands can be dealt from a deck of 52 playing cards?

17. How many three-letter permutations can be formed from the first eight letters of the alphabet (a) if repetitions are not allowed? (b) if repetitions are allowed?

18. In a seven-team baseball league, in how many ways can the top three positions in the final standings be filled?

19. In how many ways can the manager of a baseball team arrange his batting order of nine starters if he wants his best hitters in the top four positions?

20. In a baseball league of nine teams, how many games are needed to complete the schedule if each team plays 12 games with each other team?

21. How many committees consisting of four women and four men can be chosen from a group of seven women and eight men?

22. How many three-element subsets containing one vowel and two consonants can be formed from the set {a, b, c, d, e, f, g, h, i}?

23. Five associate professors are being considered for promotion to the rank of full professor, but only three will be promoted. How many different combinations of three could be promoted?

24. How many numbers of four different digits can be formed from the digits 1, 2, 3, 4, 5, 6, 7, 8, and 9 if each number must consist of two odd and two even digits?

25. How many three-element subsets containing the letter A can be formed from the set {A, B, C, D, E, F}?

26. How many four-person committees can be chosen from five women and three men if each committee must contain at least one man?

27. How many different seven-letter permutations can be formed from four identical H's and three identical T's?

28. How many different eight-letter permutations can be formed from six identical H's and two identical T's?

29. How many different nine-letter permutations can be formed from three identical A's, four identical B's, and two identical C's?

30. How many different ten-letter permutations can be formed from five identical A's, four identical B's, and one C?

31. How many different seven-letter permutations can be formed from the seven letters of the word ALGEBRA?

32. How many different 11-letter permutations can be formed from the 11 letters of the word MATHEMATICS?

33. In how many ways can x^4y^2 be written without using exponents? [*Hint*: One way is *xxxxyy*.]

34. In how many ways can $x^3y^4z^3$ be written without using exponents?

35. Ten basketball players are going to be divided into two teams of five players each for a game. In how many ways can this be done?

36. Ten basketball players are going to be divided into two teams of five in such a way that the two best players are on opposite teams. In how many ways can this be done?

37. A box contains nine good light bulbs and four defective bulbs. How many samples of three bulbs contain one defective bulb? How many samples of three bulbs contain *at least* one defective bulb?

38. How many five-person committees consisting of two juniors and three seniors can be formed from a group of six juniors and eight seniors?

39. In how many ways can six people be divided into two groups so that there are four in one group and two in the other? In how many ways can six people be divided into two groups of three each?

40. How many five-element subsets containing A and B can be formed from the set {A, B, C, D, E, F, G, H}?

41. How many four-element subsets containing A or B but not both A and B can be formed from the set {A, B, C, D, E, F, G}?

42. How many different five-person committees can be selected from nine people if two of those people refuse to serve together on a committee?

43. How many different line segments are determined by five points? By six points? By seven points? By n points?

44. **(a)** How many five-card hands consisting of two kings and three aces can be dealt from a deck of 52 playing cards?

(b) How many five-card hands consisting of three kings and two aces can be dealt from a deck of 52 playing cards?

(c) How many five-card hands consisting of three cards of one face value and two cards of another face value can be dealt from a deck of 52 playing cards?

THOUGHTS INTO WORDS

45. Explain the difference between a permutation and a combination. Give an example of each one to illustrate your explanation.

46. Your friend is having difficulty distinguishing between permutations and combinations in problem-solving situations. What might you do to help her?

FURTHER INVESTIGATIONS

47. In how many ways can six people be seated at a circular table? [*Hint*: Moving each person one place to the right (or left) does not create a new seating.]

48. The quantity $P(8, 3)$ can be expressed completely in factorial notation as follows:

$$P(8, 3) = \frac{P(8, 3) \cdot 5!}{5!} = \frac{(8 \cdot 7 \cdot 6)(5 \cdot 4 \cdot 3 \cdot 2 \cdot 1)}{5!} = \frac{8!}{5!}$$

Express each of the following in terms of factorial notation.

(a) $P(7, 3)$

(b) $P(9, 2)$

(c) $P(10, 7)$

(d) $P(n, r)$, $r \leq n$ and $0!$ is defined to be 1

49. Sometimes the formula

$$C(n, r) = \frac{n!}{r!(n - r)!}$$

is used to find the number of combinations of n things taken r at a time. Use the result from part (d) of Problem 48 and develop this formula.

50. Compute $C(7, 3)$ and $C(7, 4)$. Compute $C(8, 2)$ and $C(8, 6)$. Compute $C(9, 8)$ and $C(9, 1)$. Now argue that $C(n, r) = C(n, n - r)$ for $r \leq n$.

GRAPHING CALCULATOR ACTIVITIES

Before doing Problems 51–56, be sure that you can use your calculator to compute the number of permutations and combinations. Your calculator may possess a special sequence of keys for such computations. You may need to refer to your user's manual for this information.

51. Use your calculator to check your answers for Problems 1–12.

52. How many different five-card hands can be dealt from a deck of 52 playing cards?

53. How many different seven-card hands can be dealt from a deck of 52 playing cards?

54. How many different five-person committees can be formed from a group of 50 people?

55. How many different juries consisting of 11 people can be chosen from a group of 30 people?

56. How many seven-person committees consisting of three juniors and four seniors can be formed from 45 juniors and 53 seniors?

15.3 Probability

In order to introduce some terminology and notation, let's consider a simple experiment of tossing a regular six-sided die. There are six possible outcomes to this experiment: The 1, the 2, the 3, the 4, the 5, or the 6 will land up. This set of possible outcomes is called a "sample space," and the individual elements of the sample space are called "sample points." We will use S (sometimes with subscripts for identification purposes) to refer to a particular sample space of an experiment; then we will denote the number of sample points by $n(S)$. Thus for the experiment of tossing a die, $S = \{1, 2, 3, 4, 5, 6\}$ and $n(S) = 6$.

In general, the set of all possible outcomes of a given experiment is called the **sample space**, and the individual elements of the sample space are called **sample points**. (In this text, we will be working only with sample spaces that are finite.)

Now suppose we are interested in some of the various possible outcomes in the die-tossing experiment. For example, we might be interested in the event, *an even number comes up*. In this case we are satisfied if a 2, 4, or 6 appears on the top face of the die, and therefore the event, *an even number comes up*, is the subset $E = \{2, 4, 6\}$, where $n(E) = 3$. Perhaps, instead, we might be interested in the event, *a multiple of 3 comes up*. This event determines the subset $F = \{3, 6\}$, where $n(F) = 2$.

In general, any subset of a sample space is called an **event** or an **event space**. If the event consists of exactly one element of the sample space, then it is called a **simple event**. Any nonempty event that is not simple is called a **compound event**. A compound event can be represented as the union of simple events.

It is now possible to give a very simple definition for *probability* as we want to use the term in this text.

Definition 15.1

In an experiment where all possible outcomes in the sample space S are equally likely to occur, the **probability** of an event E is defined by

$$P(E) = \frac{n(E)}{n(S)}$$

where $n(E)$ denotes the number of elements in the event E, and $n(S)$ denotes the number of elements in the sample space S.

Many probability problems can be solved by applying Definition 15.1. Such an approach requires that we be able to determine the number of elements in the sample space and the number of elements in the event space. For example, in the die-tossing experiment, the probability of getting an even number with one toss of the die is given by

$$P(E) = \frac{n(E)}{n(S)} = \frac{3}{6} = \frac{1}{2}$$

Let's consider two examples where the number of elements in both the sample space and the event space are easy to determine.

PROBLEM 1

A coin is tossed. Find the probability that a head turns up.

Solution

Let the sample space be $S = \{H, T\}$; then $n(S) = 2$. The event of a head turning up is the subset $E = \{H\}$, so $n(E) = 1$. Therefore the probability of getting a head with one flip of a coin is given by

$$P(E) = \frac{n(E)}{n(S)} = \frac{1}{2}$$

■

PROBLEM 2

Two coins are tossed. What is the probability that *at least* one head will turn up?

Solution

For clarification purposes, let the coins be a penny and a nickel. The possible outcomes of this experiment are (1) a head on both coins, (2) a head on the penny and a tail on the nickel, (3) a tail on the penny and a head on the nickel, and (4) a tail on both coins. Using ordered-pair notation, where the first entry of a pair represents the penny and the second entry the nickel, we can write the sample space as

$$S = \{(H, H), (H, T), (T, H), (T, T)\}$$

and $n(S) = 4$.

Let E be the event of getting at least one head. Thus $E = \{(H, H), (H, T), (T, H)\}$ and $n(E) = 3$. Therefore the probability of getting at least one head with one toss of two coins is

$$P(E) = \frac{n(E)}{n(S)} = \frac{3}{4}$$

■

As you might expect, the counting techniques discussed in the first two sections of this chapter can frequently be used to solve probability problems.

PROBLEM 3

Four coins are tossed. Find the probability of getting three heads and one tail.

Solution

The sample space consists of the possible outcomes for tossing four coins. Because there are two things that can happen on each coin, by the fundamental principle of counting there are $2 \cdot 2 \cdot 2 \cdot 2 = 16$ possible outcomes for tossing four coins. Thus we know that $n(S) = 16$ without taking the time to list all of the elements. The event of getting three heads and one tail is the subset $E = \{(H, H, H, T), (H, H, T, H), (H, T, H, H), (T, H, H, H)\}$, where $n(E) = 4$. Therefore the requested probability is

$$P(E) = \frac{n(E)}{n(S)} = \frac{4}{16} = \frac{1}{4}$$

■

PROBLEM 4

Al, Bob, Chad, Dorcas, Eve, and Françoise are randomly seated in a row of six chairs. What is the probability that Al and Bob are seated in the end seats?

Solution

The sample space consists of all possible ways of seating six people in six chairs or, in other words, the permutations of six things taken six at a time. Thus $n(S) = P(6, 6) = 6! = 6 \cdot 5 \cdot 4 \cdot 3 \cdot 2 \cdot 1 = 720$.

The event space consists of all possible ways of seating the six people so that Al and Bob both occupy end seats. The number of these possibilities can be determined as follows:

Task 1 Put Al and Bob in the end seats. This can be done in two ways because Al can be on the left end and Bob on the right end, or vice versa.

Task 2 Put the other four people in the remaining four seats. This can be done in $4! = 4 \cdot 3 \cdot 2 \cdot 1 = 24$ different ways.

Therefore task 1 followed by task 2 can be done in $(2)(24) = 48$ different ways, so $n(E) = 48$. Thus the requested probability is

$$P(E) = \frac{n(E)}{n(S)} = \frac{48}{720} = \frac{1}{15}$$

■

Note that in Problem 3, by using the fundamental principle of counting to determine the number of elements in the sample space, we did not actually have to list all of the elements. For the event space, we listed the elements and counted them in the usual way. In Problem 4, we used the permutation formula $P(n, n) = n!$ to determine the number of elements in the sample space, and then we used the fundamental principle to determine the number of elements in the event space. There are no definite rules about when to list the elements and when to apply some sort of counting technique. In general, we suggest that if you do not immediately see a counting pattern for a particular problem, you should begin the listing process. If a counting pattern then emerges as you are listing the elements, use the pattern at that time.

The combination (subset) formula we developed in Section 15.2, $C(n, r) = P(n, r)/r!$, is also a very useful tool for solving certain kinds of probability problems. The next three examples illustrate some problems of this type.

PROBLEM 5

A committee of three people is randomly selected from Alice, Bjorn, Chad, Dee, and Eric. What is the probability that Alice is on the committee?

Solution

The sample space, S, consists of all possible three-person committees that can be formed from the five people. Therefore

$$n(S) = C(5, 3) = \frac{P(5, 3)}{3!} = \frac{5 \cdot 4 \cdot 3}{3 \cdot 2 \cdot 1} = 10$$

The event space, E, consists of all the three-person committees that have Alice as a member. Each of those committees contains Alice and two other people chosen from the four remaining people. Thus the number of such committees is $C(4, 2)$, so we obtain

$$n(E) = C(4, 2) = \frac{P(4, 2)}{2!} = \frac{4 \cdot 3}{2 \cdot 1} = 6$$

The requested probability is

$$P(E) = \frac{n(E)}{n(S)} = \frac{6}{10} = \frac{3}{5}$$

■

PROBLEM 6

A committee of four is chosen at random from a group of five seniors and four juniors. Find the probability that the committee will contain two seniors and two juniors.

Solution

The sample space, S, consists of all possible four-person committees that can be formed from the nine people. Thus

$$n(S) = C(9, 4) = \frac{P(9, 4)}{4!} = \frac{9 \cdot 8 \cdot 7 \cdot 6}{4 \cdot 3 \cdot 2 \cdot 1} = 126$$

The event space, E, consists of all four-person committees that contain two seniors and two juniors. They can be counted as follows.

Task 1 Choose two seniors from the five available seniors in $C(5, 2) = 10$ ways.

Task 2 Choose two juniors from the four available juniors in $C(4, 2) = 6$ ways.

Therefore there are $10 \cdot 6 = 60$ committees consisting of two seniors and two juniors. The requested probability is

$$P(E) = \frac{n(E)}{n(S)} = \frac{60}{126} = \frac{10}{21}$$

■

PROBLEM 7

Eight coins are tossed. Find the probability of getting two heads and six tails.

Solution

Because either of two things can happen on each coin, the total number of possible outcomes, $n(S)$, is $2^8 = 256$.

We can select two coins, which are to fall heads, in $C(8, 2) = 28$ ways. For each of these ways, there is only one way to select the other six coins that are to fall tails. Therefore there are $28 \cdot 1 = 28$ ways of getting two heads and six tails, so $n(E) = 28$. The requested probability is

$$P(E) = \frac{n(E)}{n(S)} = \frac{28}{256} = \frac{7}{64}$$

■

Problem Set 15.3

For Problems 1–4, *two* coins are tossed. Find the probability of tossing each of the following events:

1. One head and one tail

2. Two tails

3. At least one tail

4. No tails

For Problems 5–8, *three* coins are tossed. Find the probability of tossing each of the following events:

5. Three heads

6. Two heads and a tail

7. At least one head

8. Exactly one tail

For Problems 9–12, *four* coins are tossed. Find the probability of tossing each of the following events:

9. Four heads

10. Three heads and a tail

11. Two heads and two tails

12. At least one head

For Problems 13–16, *one* die is tossed. Find the probability of rolling each of the following events:

13. A multiple of 3

14. A prime number

15. An even number

16. A multiple of 7

For Problems 17–22, *two* dice are tossed. Find the probability of rolling each of the following events:

17. A sum of 6

18. A sum of 11

19. A sum less than 5

20. A 5 on exactly one die

21. A 4 on at least one die

22. A sum greater than 4

For Problems 23–26, *one* card is drawn from a standard deck of 52 playing cards. Find the probability of each of the following events:

23. A heart is drawn.

24. A king is drawn.

25. A spade or a diamond is drawn.

26. A red jack is drawn.

For Problems 27–30, suppose that 25 slips of paper numbered 1 to 25, inclusive, are put in a hat, and then one is drawn out at random. Find the probability of each of the following events:

27. The slip with the 5 on it is drawn.

28. A slip with an even number on it is drawn.

29. A slip with a prime number on it is drawn.

30. A slip with a multiple of 6 on it is drawn.

For Problems 31–34, suppose that a committee of two boys is to be chosen at random from the five boys Al, Bill, Carl, Dan, and Eli. Find the probability of each of the following events:

31. Dan is on the committee.

32. Dan and Eli are both on the committee.

33. Bill and Carl are not both on the committee.

34. Dan or Eli, but not both of them, is on the committee.

For Problems 35–38, suppose that a five-person committee is selected at random from the eight people Al, Barb, Chad, Dominique, Eric, Fern, George, and Harriet. Find the probability of each of the following events:

35. Al and Barb are both on the committee.

36. George is not on the committee.

37. Either Chad or Dominique, but not both, is on the committee.

38. Neither Al nor Barb is on the committee.

For Problems 39–41, suppose that a box of ten items from a manufacturing company is known to contain two defective and eight nondefective items. A sample of three items is selected at random. Find the probability of each of the following events:

39. The sample contains all nondefective items.

40. The sample contains one defective and two nondefective items.

41. The sample contains two defective and one nondefective item.

For Problems 42–60, solve each problem.

42. A building has five doors. Find the probability that two people, entering the building at random, will choose the same door.

43. Bill, Carol, and Alice are to be seated at random in a row of three seats. Find the probability that Bill and Carol will be seated side by side.

44. April, Bill, Carl, and Denise are to be seated at random in a row of four chairs. What is the probability that April and Bill will occupy the end seats?

45. A committee of four girls is to be chosen at random from the five girls Alice, Becky, Candy, Dee, and Elaine. Find the probability that Elaine is not on the committee.

46. Three boys and two girls are to be seated at random in a row of five seats. What is the probability that the boys and girls will be in alternating seats?

47. Four different mathematics books and five different history books are randomly placed on a shelf. What is the probability that all of the books on a subject are side by side?

48. Each of three letters is to be mailed in any one of five different mailboxes. What is the probability that all will be mailed in the same mailbox?

49. Randomly form a four-digit number by using the digits 2, 3, 4, and 6 once each. What is the probability that the number formed is greater than 4000?

50. Randomly select one of the 120 permutations of the letters a, b, c, d, and e. Find the probability that in the chosen permutation, the letter a precedes the b (the a is to the left of the b).

51. A committee of four is chosen at random from a group of six women and five men. Find the probability that the committee contains two women and two men.

52. A committee of three is chosen at random from a group of four women and five men. Find the probability that the committee contains at least one man.

53. Ahmed, Bob, Carl, Dan, Ed, Frank, Gino, Harry, Julio, and Mike are randomly divided into two five-man teams for a basketball game. What is the probability that Ahmed, Bob, and Carl are on the same team?

54. Seven coins are tossed. Find the probability of getting four heads and three tails.

55. Nine coins are tossed. Find the probability of getting three heads and six tails.

56. Six coins are tossed. Find the probability of getting at least four heads.

57. Five coins are tossed. Find the probability of getting no more than three heads.

58. Each arrangement of the 11 letters of the word MISSISSIPPI is put on a slip of paper and placed in a hat. One slip is drawn at random from the hat. Find the probability that the slip contains an arrangement of the letters with the four S's at the beginning.

59. Each arrangement of the seven letters of the word OSMOSIS is put on a slip of paper and placed in a hat. One slip is drawn at random from the hat. Find the probability that the slip contains an arrangement of the letters with an O at the beginning and an O at the end.

60. Consider all possible arrangements of three identical H's and three identical T's. Suppose that one of these arrangements is selected at random. What is the probability that the selected arrangement has the three H's in consecutive positions?

THOUGHTS INTO WORDS

61. Explain the concepts of sample space and event space.

62. Why must probability answers fall between 0 and 1, inclusive? Give an example of a situation for which the probability is 0. Also give an example for which the probability is 1.

FURTHER INVESTIGATIONS

In Problem 7 of Section 15.2, we found that there are 2,598,960 different five-card hands that can be dealt from a deck of 52 playing cards. Therefore, probabilities for certain kinds of five-card poker hands can be calculated by using 2,598,960 as the number of elements in the sample space. For Problems 63–71, determine the number of different five-card poker hands of the indicated type that can be obtained.

63. A straight flush (five cards in sequence and of the same suit; aces are both low and high, so A2345 and 10JQKA are both acceptable)

64. Four of a kind (four of the same face value, such as four kings)

65. A full house (three cards of one face value and two cards of another face value)

66. A flush (five cards of the same suit but not in sequence)

67. A straight (five cards in sequence but not all of the same suit)

68. Three of a kind (three cards of one face value and two cards of two different face values)

69. Two pairs

70. Exactly one pair

71. No pairs

15.4 Some Properties of Probability; Expected Values

There are several basic properties that are useful in the study of probability from both a theoretical and a computational viewpoint. We will discuss two of these properties at this time and some additional ones in the next section. The first property may seem to state the obvious, but it still needs to be mentioned.

Property 15.1

For all events E,

$$0 \leq P(E) \leq 1$$

Property 15.1 simply states that probabilities must fall in the range from 0 to 1, inclusive. This seems reasonable because $P(E) = n(E)/n(S)$, and E is a subset of S. The next two examples illustrate circumstances where $P(E) = 0$ and $P(E) = 1$.

PROBLEM 1 Toss a regular six-sided die. What is the probability of getting a 7?

Solution

The sample space is $S = \{1, 2, 3, 4, 5, 6\}$, thus $n(S) = 6$. The event space is $E = \varnothing$, so $n(E) = 0$. Therefore the probability of getting a 7 is

$$P(E) = \frac{n(E)}{n(S)} = \frac{0}{6} = 0$$

■

PROBLEM 2 What is the probability of getting a head or a tail with one flip of a coin?

Solution

The sample space is $S = \{\text{H}, \text{T}\}$, and the event space is $E = \{\text{H}, \text{T}\}$. Therefore $n(S) = n(E) = 2$, and

$$P(E) = \frac{n(E)}{n(S)} = \frac{2}{2} = 1$$

■

An event that has a probability of 1 is sometimes called **certain success**, and an event with a probability of 0 is called **certain failure**.

It should also be mentioned that Property 15.1 serves as a check for reasonableness of answers. In other words, when computing probabilities, we know that our answer must fall between 0 and 1, inclusive. Any other probability answer is simply not reasonable.

Complementary Events

Complementary events are complementary sets such that S, the sample space, serves as the universal set. The following examples illustrate this idea.

Sample space	Event space	Complement of event space
$S = \{1, 2, 3, 4, 5, 6\}$	$E = \{1, 2\}$	$E' = \{3, 4, 5, 6\}$
$S = \{\text{H}, \text{T}\}$	$E = \{\text{T}\}$	$E' = \{\text{H}\}$
$S = \{2, 3, 4, \ldots, 12\}$	$E = \{2, 3, 4\}$	$E' = \{5, 6, 7, \ldots, 12\}$
$S = \{1, 2, 3, \ldots, 25\}$	$E = \{3, 4, 5, \ldots, 25\}$	$E' = \{1, 2\}$

In each case, note that E' (the complement of E) consists of all elements of S that are *not* in E. Thus E and E' are called *complementary events*. Also note that for each example, $P(E) + P(E') = 1$. We can state the following general property:

Property 15.2

If E is any event of a sample space S, and E' is the complementary event, then

$$P(E) + P(E') = 1$$

From a computational viewpoint, Property 15.2 provides us with a double-barreled attack on some probability problems. That is, once we compute either $P(E)$ or $P(E')$, we can determine the other one simply by subtracting from 1. For example, suppose that for a particular problem we can determine that $P(E) = \frac{3}{13}$. Then we immediately know that $P(E') = 1 - P(E) = 1 - \frac{3}{13} = \frac{10}{13}$. The following examples further illustrate the usefulness of Property 15.2.

PROBLEM 3

Two dice are tossed. Find the probability of getting a sum greater than 3.

Solution

Let S be the familiar sample space of ordered pairs for this problem, where $n(S) = 36$. Let E be the event of obtaining a sum greater than 3. Then E' is the event of obtaining a sum less than or equal to 3; that is, $E' = \{(1, 1), (1, 2), (2, 1)\}$. Thus

$$P(E') = \frac{n(E')}{n(S)} = \frac{3}{36} = \frac{1}{12}$$

From this, we conclude that

$$P(E) = 1 - P(E') = 1 - \frac{1}{12} = \frac{11}{12}$$

■

PROBLEM 4

Toss three coins and find the probability of getting at least one head.

Solution

The sample space, S, consists of all possible outcomes for tossing three coins. Using the fundamental principle of counting, we know that there are $(2)(2)(2) = 8$ outcomes, so $n(S) = 8$. Let E be the event of getting at least one head. Then E' is the complementary event of not getting any heads. The set E' is easy to list: $E' = \{(\text{T, T, T})\}$. Thus $n(E') = 1$ and $P(E') = \frac{1}{8}$. From this, $P(E)$ can be determined to be

$$P(E) = 1 - P(E') = 1 - \frac{1}{8} = \frac{7}{8}$$

■

PROBLEM 5

A three-person committee is chosen at random from a group of five women and four men. Find the probability that the committee contains at least one woman.

Solution

Let the sample space, S, be the set of all possible three-person committees that can be formed from nine people. There are $C(9, 3) = 84$ such committees; therefore $n(S) = 84$.

Let E be the event, *the committee contains at least one woman*. Then E' is the complementary event, *the committee contains all men*. Thus E' consists of all three-man committees that can be formed from four men. There are $C(4, 3) = 4$ such committees; thus $n(E') = 4$. We have

$$P(E') = \frac{n(E')}{n(S)} = \frac{4}{84} = \frac{1}{21}$$

which determines $P(E)$ to be

$$P(E) = 1 - P(E') = 1 - \frac{1}{21} = \frac{20}{21}$$

■

The concepts of **set intersection** and **set union** play an important role in the study of probability. If E and F are two events in a sample space S, then $E \cap F$ is the event consisting of all sample points of S that are in both E and F as indicated in Figure 15.2. Likewise, $E \cup F$ is the event consisting of all sample points of S that are in E or F, or both, as shown in Figure 15.3.

In Figure 15.4, there are 47 sample points in E, 38 sample points in F, and 15 sample points in $E \cap F$. How many sample points are there in $E \cup F$? Simply adding the number of points in E and F would result in counting the 15 points in

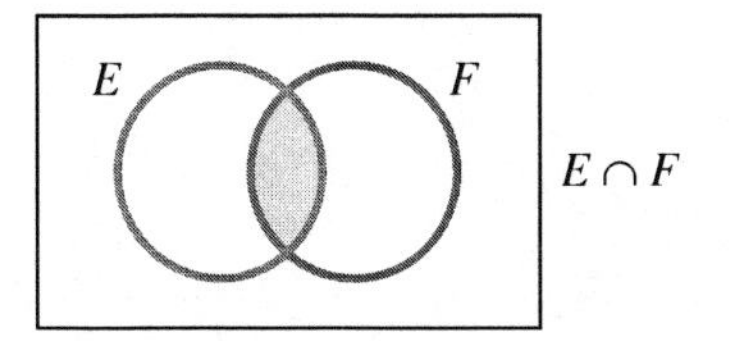

Figure 15.2

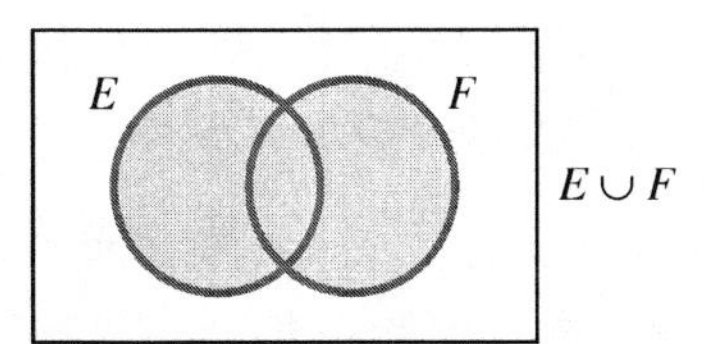

Figure 15.3

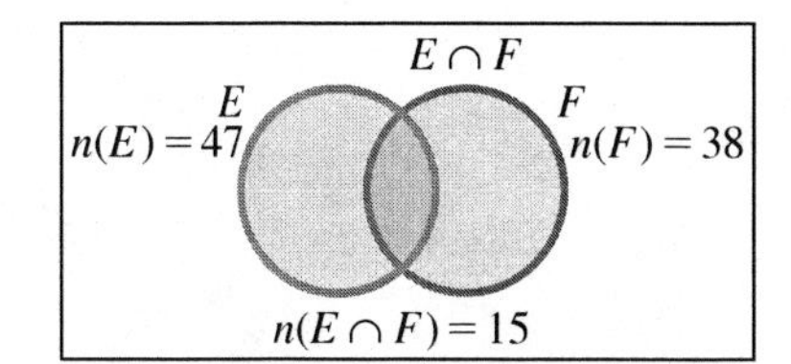

Figure 15.4

$E \cap F$ twice. Therefore, 15 must be subtracted from the total number of points in E and F, yielding $47 + 38 - 15 = 70$ points in $E \cup F$. We can state the following general counting property:

$$n(E \cup F) = n(E) + n(F) - n(E \cap F)$$

If we divide both sides of this equation by $n(S)$, we obtain the following probability property:

Property 15.3

For events E and F of a sample space S,

$$P(E \cup F) = P(E) + P(F) - P(E \cap F)$$

PROBLEM 6

What is the probability of getting an odd number or a prime number with one toss of a die?

Solution

Let $S = \{1, 2, 3, 4, 5, 6\}$ be the sample space, $E = \{1, 3, 5\}$ the event of getting an odd number, and $F = \{2, 3, 5\}$ the event of getting a prime number. Then $E \cap F = \{3, 5\}$, and using Property 15.3, we obtain

$$P(E \cup F) = \frac{3}{6} + \frac{3}{6} - \frac{2}{6} = \frac{4}{6} = \frac{2}{3}$$

■

PROBLEM 7

Toss three coins. What is the probability of getting at least two heads or exactly one tail?

Solution

Using the fundamental principle of counting, we know that there are $2 \cdot 2 \cdot 2 = 8$ possible outcomes of tossing three coins; thus $n(S) = 8$. Let

$$E = \{(H, H, H), (H, H, T), (H, T, H), (T, H, H)\}$$

be the event of getting at least two heads, and let

$$F = \{(H, H, T), (H, T, H), (T, H, H)\}$$

be the event of getting exactly one tail. Then

$$E \cap F = \{(H, H, T), (H, T, H), (T, H, H)\}$$

and we can compute $P(E \cup F)$ as follows.

$$P(E \cup F) = P(E) + P(F) - P(E \cap F)$$

$$= \frac{4}{8} + \frac{3}{8} - \frac{3}{8}$$

$$= \frac{4}{8} = \frac{1}{2}$$

In Property 15.3, if $E \cap F = \varnothing$, then the events E and F are said to be **mutually exclusive**. In other words, mutually exclusive events are events that cannot occur at the same time. For example, when we roll a die, the event of getting a 4 and the event of getting a 5 are mutually exclusive; they cannot both happen on the same roll. If $E \cap F = \varnothing$, then $P(E \cap F) = 0$, and Property 15.3 becomes **$P(E \cup F) = P(E) + P(F)$ for mutually exclusive events.**

PROBLEM 8

Suppose we have a jar that contains five white, seven green, and nine red marbles. If one marble is drawn at random from the jar, find the probability that it is white or green.

Solution

The events of drawing a white marble and drawing a green marble are mutually exclusive. Therefore the probability of drawing a white or a green marble is

$$\frac{5}{21} + \frac{7}{21} = \frac{12}{21} = \frac{4}{7}$$

Note that in the solution for Problem 8, we did not explicitly name and list the elements of the sample space or event spaces. It was obvious that the sample space contained 21 elements (21 marbles in the jar) and that the event spaces contained five elements (five white marbles) and seven elements (seven green marbles). Thus it was not necessary to name and list the sample space and event spaces.

PROBLEM 9

Suppose that the data in the following table represent the results of a survey of 1000 drivers after a holiday weekend.

	Rain (R)	No rain (R')	Total
Accident (A)	35	10	45
No accident (A')	450	505	955
Total	485	515	1000

If a person is selected at random, what is the probability that the person was in an accident or that it rained?

Solution

First, let's form a **probability table** by dividing each entry by 1000, the total number surveyed.

	Rain (R)	No rain (R')	Total
Accident (A)	0.035	0.010	0.045
No accident (A')	0.450	0.505	0.955
Total	0.485	0.515	1.000

Now we can use Property 15.3 and compute $P(A \cup R)$.

$$\begin{aligned} P(A \cup R) &= P(A) + P(R) - P(A \cap R) \\ &= 0.045 + 0.485 - 0.035 \\ &= 0.495 \end{aligned}$$

■

■ Expected Value

Suppose we toss a coin 500 times. We would expect to get approximately 250 heads. In other words, because the probability of getting a head with one toss of a coin is $\frac{1}{2}$, in 500 tosses we should get approximately $500\left(\frac{1}{2}\right) = 250$ heads. The word "approximately" conveys a key idea. As we know from experience, it is possible to toss a coin several times and get all heads. However, with a large number of tosses, things should average out so that we get about equal numbers of heads and tails.

As another example, consider the fact that the probability of getting a sum of 6 with one toss of a pair of dice is $\frac{5}{36}$. Therefore, if a pair of dice is tossed 360 times, we should expect to get a sum of 6 approximately $360\left(\frac{5}{36}\right) = 50$ times.

Let us now define the concept of *expected value.*

Definition 15.2

If the k possible outcomes of an experiment are assigned the values $x_1, x_2, x_3, \ldots, x_k$, and if they occur with probabilities of $p_1, p_2, p_3, \ldots, p_k$, respectively, then the **expected value** of the experiment (E_v) is given by

$$E_v = x_1p_1 + x_2p_2 + x_3p_3 + \cdots + x_kp_k$$

The concept of expected value (also called **mathematical expectation**) is used in a variety of probability situations that deal with such things as fairness of games and decision making in business ventures. Let's consider some examples.

PROBLEM 10

Suppose that you buy one ticket in a lottery where 1000 tickets are sold. Furthermore, suppose that three prizes are awarded: one of \$500, one of \$300, and one of \$100. What is your mathematical expectation?

Solution

Because you bought one ticket, the probability of you winning \$500 is $\frac{1}{1000}$; the probability of you winning \$300 is $\frac{1}{1000}$; and the probability of you winning \$100 is $\frac{1}{1000}$. Multiplying each of these probabilities by the corresponding prize money and then adding the results yields your mathematical expectation.

$$E_v = \$500\left(\frac{1}{100}\right) + \$300\left(\frac{1}{1000}\right) + \$100\left(\frac{1}{100}\right)$$

$$= \$0.50 + \$0.30 + \$0.10$$

$$= \$0.90$$

In Problem 10, if you pay more than \$0.90 for a ticket, then it is not a **fair game** from your standpoint. If the price of the game is included in the calculation of the expected value, then a fair game is defined to be one where the expected value is zero.

PROBLEM 11

A player pays \$5 to play a game where the probability of winning is $\frac{1}{5}$ and the probability of losing is $\frac{4}{5}$. If the player wins the game, he receives \$25. Is this a fair game for the player?

Solution

From Definition 15.2, let $x_1 = \$20$, which represents the \$25 won minus the \$5 paid to play, and let $x_2 = -\$5$, the amount paid to play the game. We are also given that $p_1 = \frac{1}{5}$ and $p_2 = \frac{4}{5}$. Thus the expected value is

$$E_v = \$20\left(\frac{1}{5}\right) + (-\$5)\left(\frac{4}{5}\right)$$

$$= \$4 - \$4$$

$$= 0$$

Because the expected value is zero, it is a fair game.

PROBLEM 12

Suppose you are interested in insuring a diamond ring for \$2000 against theft. An insurance company charges a premium of \$25 per year, claiming that there is a probability of 0.01 that the ring will be stolen during the year. What is your expected gain or loss if you take out the insurance?

Solution

From Definition 15.2, let $x_1 = \$1975$, which represents the \$2000 minus the cost of the premium, \$25, and let $x_2 = -\$25$. We also are given that $p_1 = 0.01$, so $p_2 = 1 - 0.01 = 0.99$. Thus the expected value is

$$\begin{aligned} E_v &= \$1975(0.01) + (-\$25)(0.99) \\ &= \$19.75 - \$24.75 \\ &= -\$5.00 \end{aligned}$$

This means that if you insure with this company over many years, and the circumstances remain the same, you will have an average net loss of \$5 per year. ■

Problem Set 15.4

For Problems 1–4, *two* dice are tossed. Find the probability of rolling each of the following events:

1. A sum of 6

2. A sum greater than 2

3. A sum less than 8

4. A sum greater than 1

For Problems 5–8, *three* dice are tossed. Find the probability of rolling each of the following events:

5. A sum of 3

6. A sum greater than 4

7. A sum less than 17

8. A sum greater than 18

For Problems 9–12, *four* coins are tossed. Find the probability of getting each of the following events:

9. Four heads

10. Three heads and a tail

11. At least one tail

12. At least one head

For Problems 13–16, *five* coins are tossed. Find the probability of getting each of the following events:

13. Five tails

14. Four heads and a tail

15. At least one tail

16. At least two heads

For Problems 17–23, solve each problem.

17. Toss a pair of dice. What is the probability of not getting a double?

18. The probability that a certain horse will win the Kentucky Derby is $\frac{1}{20}$. What is the probability that it will lose the race?

19. One card is randomly drawn from a deck of 52 playing cards. What is the probability that it is not an ace?

20. Six coins are tossed. Find the probability of getting at least two heads.

21. A subset of two letters is chosen at random from the set {a, b, c, d, e, f, g, h, i}. Find the probability that the subset contains at least one vowel.

22. A two-person committee is chosen at random from a group of four men and three women. Find the probability that the committee contains at least one man.

23. A three-person committee is chosen at random from a group of seven women and five men. Find the probability that the committee contains at least one man.

For Problems 24–27, one die is tossed. Find the probability of rolling each of the following events:

24. A 3 or an odd number

25. A 2 or an odd number

26. An even number or a prime number

27. An odd number or a multiple of 3

For Problems 28–31, two dice are tossed. Find the probability of rolling each of the following events:

28. A double or a sum of 6

29. A sum of 10 or a sum greater than 8

30. A sum of 5 or a sum greater than 10

31. A double or a sum of 7

For Problems 32–56, solve each problem.

32. Two coins are tossed. Find the probability of getting exactly one head or at least one tail.

33. Three coins are tossed. Find the probability of getting at least two heads or exactly one tail.

34. A jar contains seven white, six blue, and ten red marbles. If one marble is drawn at random from the jar, find the probability that (a) the marble is white or blue; (b) the marble is white or red; (c) the marble is blue or red.

35. A coin and a die are tossed. Find the probability of getting a head on the coin or a 2 on the die.

36. A card is randomly drawn from a deck of 52 playing cards. Find the probability that it is a red card or a face card. (Jacks, queens, and kings are the face cards.)

37. The data in the following table represent the results of a survey of 1000 drivers after a holiday weekend.

	Rain (R)	No rain (R')	Total
Accident (A)	45	15	60
No accident (A')	350	590	940
Total	395	605	1000

If a person is selected at random from those surveyed, find the probability of each of the following events. (Express the probabilities in decimal form.)
(a) The person was in an accident or it rained.
(b) The person was not in an accident or it rained.
(c) The person was not in an accident or it did not rain.

38. One hundred people were surveyed, and one question pertained to their educational background. The results of this question are given in the following table.

	Female (F)	Male (F')	Total
College degree (D)	30	20	50
No college degree (D')	15	35	50
Total	45	55	100

If a person is selected at random from those surveyed, find the probability of each of the following events. Express the probabilities in decimal form.
(a) The person is female or has a college degree.
(b) The person is male or does not have a college degree.
(c) The person is female or does not have a college degree.

39. In a recent election there were 1000 eligible voters. They were asked to vote on two issues, A and B. The results were as follows: 300 people voted for A, 400 people voted for B, and 175 voted for both A and B. If one person is chosen at random from the 1000 eligible voters, find the probability that the person voted for A or B.

40. A company has 500 employees among whom 200 are females, 15 are high-level executives, and 7 of the high-level executives are females. If one of the 500 employees is chosen at random, find the probability that the person chosen is female or is a high-level executive.

41. A die is tossed 360 times. How many times would you expect to get a 6?

42. Two dice are tossed 360 times. How many times would you expect to get a sum of 5?

43. Two dice are tossed 720 times. How many times would you expect to get a sum greater than 9?

44. Four coins are tossed 80 times. How many times would you expect to get one head and three tails?

45. Four coins are tossed 144 times. How many times would you expect to get four tails?

46. Two dice are tossed 300 times. How many times would you expect to get a double?

47. Three coins are tossed 448 times. How many times would you expect to get three heads?

48. Suppose 5000 tickets are sold in a lottery. There are three prizes: The first is \$1000, the second is \$500, and the third is \$100. What is the mathematical expectation of winning?

49. Your friend challenges you with the following game: You are to roll a pair of dice, and he will give you \$5 if you roll a sum of 2 or 12, \$2 if you roll a sum of 3 or 11, \$1 if you roll a sum of 4 or 10. Otherwise you are to pay him \$1. Should you play the game?

50. A contractor bids on a building project. There is a probability of 0.8 that he can show a profit of \$30,000 and a probability of 0.2 that he will have to absorb a loss of \$10,000. What is his mathematical expectation?

51. Suppose a person tosses two coins and receives \$5 if 2 heads come up, receives \$2 if 1 head and 1 tail come up, and has to pay \$2 if 2 tails come up. Is it a fair game for him?

52. A "wheel of fortune" is divided into four colors: red, white, blue, and yellow. The probability of the spinner landing on each of the colors and the money received is given by the following chart. The price to spin the wheel is \$1.50. Is it a fair game?

Color	Probability of landing on the color	Money received for landing on the color
Red	$\frac{4}{10}$	\$.50
White	$\frac{3}{10}$	1.00
Blue	$\frac{2}{10}$	2.00
Yellow	$\frac{1}{10}$	5.00

53. A contractor estimates a probability of 0.7 of making \$20,000 on a building project and a probability of 0.3 of losing \$10,000 on the project. What is his mathematical expectation?

54. A farmer estimates his corn crop at 30,000 bushels. On the basis of past experience, he also estimates a probability of $\frac{3}{5}$ that he will make a profit of \$0.50 per bushel and a probability of $\frac{1}{5}$ of losing \$0.30 per bushel. What is his expected income from the corn crop?

55. Bill finds that the annual premium for insuring a stereo system for \$2500 against theft is \$75. If the probability that the set will be stolen during the year is 0.02, what is Bill's expected gain or loss by taking out the insurance?

56. Sandra finds that the annual premium for a \$2000 insurance policy against the theft of a painting is \$100. If the probability that the painting will be stolen during the year is 0.01, what is Sandra's expected gain or loss in taking out the insurance?

THOUGHTS INTO WORDS

57. If the probability of some event happening is 0.4, what is the probability of the event not happening? Explain your answer.

58. Explain each of the following concepts to a friend who missed class the day this section was discussed: using complementary events to determine probabilities, using union and intersection of sets to determine probabilities, and using expected value to determine the fairness of a game.

FURTHER INVESTIGATIONS

The term **odds** is sometimes used to express a probability statement. For example, we might say, "the odds in favor of the Cubs winning the pennant are 5 to 1," or "the odds against the Mets winning the pennant are 50 to 1." *Odds in* *favor* and *odds against* for equally likely outcomes can be defined as follows:

$$\text{Odds in favor} = \frac{\text{Number of favorable outcomes}}{\text{Number of unfavorable outcomes}}$$

$$\text{Odds against} = \frac{\text{Number of unfavorable outcomes}}{\text{Number of favorable outcomes}}$$

We have used the fractional form to define odds; however, in practice, the *to* vocabulary is commonly used. Thus the odds in favor of rolling a 4 with one roll of a die are usually stated as *1 to 5* instead of $\frac{1}{5}$. The odds against rolling a 4 are stated as *5 to 1*.

The *odds in favor of* statement about the Cubs means that there are 5 favorable outcomes compared to 1 unfavorable, or a total of 6 possible outcomes, so the *5 to 1 in favor of* statement also means that the probability of the Cubs winning the pennant is $\frac{5}{6}$. Likewise, the *50 to 1 against* statement about the Mets means that the probability that the Mets will not win the pennant is $\frac{50}{51}$.

Odds are usually stated in reduced form. For example, odds of 6 to 4 are usually stated as 3 to 2. Likewise, a fraction representing probability is reduced before being changed to a statement about odds.

59. What are the odds in favor of getting three heads with a toss of three coins?

60. What are the odds against getting four tails with a toss of four coins?

61. What are the odds against getting three heads and two tails with a toss of five coins?

62. What are the odds in favor of getting four heads and two tails with a toss of six coins?

63. What are the odds in favor of getting a sum of 5 with one toss of a pair of dice?

64. What are the odds against getting a sum greater than 5 with one toss of a pair of dice?

65. Suppose that one card is drawn at random from a deck of 52 playing cards. Find the odds against drawing a red card.

66. Suppose that one card is drawn at random from a deck of 52 playing cards. Find the odds in favor of drawing an ace or a king.

67. If $P(E) = \frac{4}{7}$ for some event E, find the odds in favor of E happening.

68. If $P(E) = \frac{5}{9}$ for some event E, find the odds against E happening.

69. Suppose that there is a predicted 40% chance of freezing rain. State the prediction in terms of the odds against getting freezing rain.

70. Suppose that there is a predicted 20% chance of thunderstorms. State the prediction in terms of the odds in favor of getting thunderstorms.

71. If the odds against an event happening are 5 to 2, find the probability that the event will occur.

72. The odds against Belly Dancer winning the fifth race are 20 to 9. What is the probability of Belly Dancer winning the fifth race?

73. The odds in favor of the Mets winning the pennant are stated as 7 to 5. What is the probability of the Mets winning the pennant?

74. The following chart contains some poker-hand probabilities. Complete the last column, "Odds Against Being Dealt This Hand." Note that fractions are reduced before being changed to odds.

5-Card hand	Probability of being dealt this hand	Odds against being dealt this hand
Straight flush	$\frac{40}{2{,}598{,}960} = \frac{1}{64{,}974}$	64,973 to 1
Four of a kind	$\frac{624}{2{,}598{,}960} =$	
Full house	$\frac{3744}{2{,}598{,}960} =$	
Flush	$\frac{5108}{2{,}598{,}960} =$	
Straight	$\frac{10{,}200}{2{,}598{,}960} =$	
Three of a kind	$\frac{54{,}912}{2{,}598{,}960} =$	
Two pairs	$\frac{123{,}552}{2{,}598{,}960} =$	
One pair	$\frac{1{,}098{,}240}{2{,}598{,}960} =$	
No pairs	$\frac{1{,}302{,}540}{2{,}598{,}960} =$	

15.5 Conditional Probability: Dependent and Independent Events

Two events are often related in such a way that the probability of one of them may vary depending on whether the other event has occurred. For example, the probability of rain may change drastically if additional information is obtained indicating a front moving through the area. Mathematically, the additional information about the front changes the sample space for the probability of rain.

In general, the probability of the occurrence of an event E, given the occurrence of another event F, is called a **conditional probability** and is denoted $P(E|F)$. Let's look at a simple example and use it to motivate a definition for conditional probability.

What is the probability of rolling a prime number in one roll of a die? Let $S = \{1, 2, 3, 4, 5, 6\}$, so $n(S) = 6$; and let $E = \{2, 3, 5\}$, so $n(E) = 3$. Therefore

$$P(E) = \frac{n(E)}{n(S)} = \frac{3}{6} = \frac{1}{2}$$

Next, what is the probability of rolling a prime number in one roll of a die, *given that an odd number has turned up*? Let $F = \{1, 3, 5\}$ be the new sample space of odd numbers. Then $n(F) = 3$. We are now interested in only that part of E (rolling a prime number) that is also in F—in other words, $E \cap F$. Therefore, because $E \cap F = \{3, 5\}$, the probability of E given F is

$$P(E|F) = \frac{n(E \cap F)}{n(F)} = \frac{2}{3}$$

When we divide both the numerator and the denominator of $n(E \cap F)/n(F)$ by $n(S)$, we obtain

$$\frac{\dfrac{n(E \cap F)}{n(S)}}{\dfrac{n(F)}{n(S)}} = \frac{P(E \cap F)}{P(F)}$$

Therefore we can state the following general definition of the conditional probability of E given F for arbitrary events E and F:

Definition 15.3

$$P(E|F) = \frac{P(E \cap F)}{P(F)}, \qquad P(F) \neq 0$$

In a problem in the previous section, the following probability table was formed relative to car accidents and weather conditions on a holiday weekend.

	Rain (R)	No rain (R')	Total
Accident (A)	0.035	0.010	0.045
No accident (A')	0.450	0.505	0.955
Total	0.485	0.515	1.000

Some conditional probabilities that can be calculated from the table follow:

$$P(A|R) = \frac{P(A \cap R)}{P(R)} = \frac{0.035}{0.485} = \frac{35}{485} = \frac{7}{97}$$

$$P(A'|R) = \frac{P(A' \cap R)}{P(R)} = \frac{0.450}{0.485} = \frac{450}{485} = \frac{90}{97}$$

$$P(A|R') = \frac{P(A \cap R')}{P(R')} = \frac{0.010}{0.515} = \frac{10}{515} = \frac{2}{103}$$

Note that the probability of an accident given that it was raining, $P(A|R)$, is greater than the probability of an accident given that it was not raining, $P(A|R')$. This seems reasonable.

PROBLEM 1

A die is tossed. Find the probability that a 4 came up if it is known that an even number turned up.

Solution

Let E be the event of rolling a 4, and let F be the event of rolling an even number. Therefore $E = \{4\}$ and $F = \{2, 4, 6\}$, from which we obtain $E \cap F = \{4\}$. Using Definition 15.3, we obtain

$$P(E|F) = \frac{P(E \cap F)}{P(F)} = \frac{\frac{1}{6}}{\frac{3}{6}} = \frac{1}{3}$$

■

PROBLEM 2

Suppose the probability that a student will enroll in a mathematics course is 0.45, the probability that he or she will enroll in a science course is 0.38, and the probability that he or she will enroll in both courses is 0.26. Find the probability that a student will enroll in a mathematics course, given that he or she is also enrolled in a science course. Also, find the probability that a student will enroll in a science course, given that he or she is enrolled in mathematics.

Solution

Let M be the event, *will enroll in mathematics*, and let S be the event, *will enroll in science*. Therefore, using Definition 10.3, we obtain

$$P(M|S) = \frac{P(M \cap S)}{P(S)} = \frac{0.26}{0.38} = \frac{26}{38} = \frac{13}{19}$$

and

$$P(S|M) = \frac{P(S \cap M)}{P(M)} = \frac{0.26}{0.45} = \frac{26}{45}$$

■

Independent and Dependent Events

Suppose that, when computing a conditional probability, we find that

$$P(E|F) = P(E)$$

This means that the probability of E is not affected by the occurrence or nonoccurrence of F. In such a situation, we say that event E is *independent* of event F. It can be shown that if event E is independent of event F, then F is also independent of E; thus E and F are referred to as **independent events**. Furthermore, from the equations

$$P(E|F) = \frac{P(E \cap F)}{P(F)} \quad \text{and} \quad P(E|F) = P(E)$$

we see that

$$\frac{P(E \cap F)}{P(F)} = P(E)$$

which can be written

$$P(E \cap F) = P(E)P(F)$$

Therefore we state the following general definition:

Definition 15.4

Two events E and F are said to be **independent** if and only if

$$P(E \cap F) = P(E)P(F)$$

Two events that are not independent are called **dependent events**.

In the probability table preceding Problem 1, we see that $P(A) = 0.045$, $P(R) = 0.485$, and $P(A \cap R) = 0.035$. Because

$$P(A)P(R) = (0.045)(0.485) = 0.021825$$

and this does not equal $P(A \cap R)$, the events A (have a car accident) and R (rainy conditions) are not independent. This is not too surprising; we would certainly expect rainy conditions and automobile accidents to be related.

PROBLEM 3

Suppose we roll a white die and a red die. If we let E be the event, *we roll a 4 on the white die*, and if we let F be the event, *we roll a 6 on the red die*. Are E and F independent events?

Solution

The sample space for rolling a pair of dice has (6)(6) = 36 elements. Using ordered-pair notation, where the first entry represents the white die and the second entry the red die, we can list events E and F as follows:

$$E = \{(4, 1), (4, 2), (4, 3), (4, 4), (4, 5), (4, 6)\}$$

$$F = \{(1, 6), (2, 6), (3, 6), (4, 6), (5, 6), (6, 6)\}$$

Therefore $E \cap F = \{(4, 6)\}$. Because $P(F) = \frac{1}{6}$, $P(E) = \frac{1}{6}$, and $P(E \cap F) = \frac{1}{36}$, we see that $P(E \cap F) = P(E)P(F)$, and the events E and F are independent. ■

PROBLEM 4

Two coins are tossed. Let E be the event, *toss not more than one head*, and let F be the event, *toss at least one of each face*. Are these events independent?

Solution

The sample space has (2)(2) = 4 elements. The events E and F can be listed as follows:

$$E = \{(\text{H}, \text{T}), (\text{T}, \text{H}), (\text{T}, \text{T})\}$$

$$F = \{(\text{H}, \text{T}), (\text{T}, \text{H})\}$$

Therefore $E \cap F = \{(\text{H}, \text{T}), (\text{T}, \text{H})\}$. Because $P(E) = \frac{3}{4}$, $P(F) = \frac{1}{2}$, and $P(E \cap F) = \frac{1}{2}$, we see that $P(E \cap F) \neq P(E)P(F)$, so the events E and F are dependent. ■

Sometimes the independence issue can be decided by the physical nature of the events in the problem. For instance, in Problem 3, it should seem evident that rolling a 4 on the white die is not affected by rolling a 6 on the red die. However, as in Problem 4, the description of the events may not clearly indicate whether the events are dependent.

From a problem-solving viewpoint, the following two statements are very helpful.

1. If E and F are independent events, then

$$P(E \cap F) = P(E)P(F)$$

(This property generalizes to any finite number of independent events.)

2. If E and F are dependent events, then

$$P(E \cap F) = P(E)P(F|E)$$

Let's analyze some problems using these ideas.

PROBLEM 5

A die is rolled three times. (This is equivalent to rolling three dice once each.) What is the probability of getting a 6 all three times?

Solution

The events of a 6 on the first roll, a 6 on the second roll, and a 6 on the third roll are independent events. Therefore the probability of getting three 6's is

$$\left(\frac{1}{6}\right)\left(\frac{1}{6}\right)\left(\frac{1}{6}\right) = \frac{1}{216}$$

■

PROBLEM 6

A jar contains five white, seven green, and nine red marbles. If two marbles are drawn in succession *without replacement*, find the probability that both marbles are white.

Solution

Let E be the event of drawing a white marble on the first draw, and let F be the event of drawing a white marble on the second draw. Because the marble drawn first is not to be replaced before the second marble is drawn, we have dependent events. Therefore

$$P(E \cap F) = P(E)P(F|E)$$

$$= \left(\frac{5}{21}\right)\left(\frac{4}{20}\right) = \frac{20}{420} = \frac{1}{21}$$

$P(F|E)$ means the probability of drawing a white marble on the second draw, given that a white marble was obtained on the first draw.

■

The concept of *mutually exclusive events* may also enter the picture when we are working with independent or dependent events. Our final problems of this section illustrate this idea.

PROBLEM 7

A coin is tossed three times. Find the probability of getting two heads and one tail.

Solution

Two heads and one tail can be obtained in three different ways: (1) HHT (head on first toss, head on second toss, and tail on third toss), (2) HTH, and (3) THH. Thus we have three *mutually exclusive* events, each of which can be broken into *independent* events: first toss, second toss, and third toss. Therefore the probability can be computed as follows:

$$\left(\frac{1}{2}\right)\left(\frac{1}{2}\right)\left(\frac{1}{2}\right) + \left(\frac{1}{2}\right)\left(\frac{1}{2}\right)\left(\frac{1}{2}\right) + \left(\frac{1}{2}\right)\left(\frac{1}{2}\right)\left(\frac{1}{2}\right) = \frac{3}{8}$$

■

PROBLEM 8

A jar contains five white, seven green, and nine red marbles. If two marbles are drawn in succession *without replacement*, find the probability that one of them is white and the other is green.

Solution

The drawing of a white marble and a green marble can occur in two different ways: (1) by drawing a white marble first and then a green, and (2) by drawing a green marble first and then a white. Thus we have two mutually exclusive events, each of which is broken into two *dependent* events: first draw and second draw. Therefore the probability can be computed as follows:

$$\left(\frac{5}{21}\right)\left(\frac{7}{20}\right) + \left(\frac{7}{21}\right)\left(\frac{5}{20}\right) = \frac{70}{420} = \frac{1}{6}$$

White on first draw; Green on second draw; Green on first draw; White on second draw ■

PROBLEM 9

Two cards are drawn in succession *with replacement* from a deck of 52 playing cards. Find the probability of drawing a jack and a queen.

Solution

Drawing a jack and a queen can occur in two different ways: (1) a jack on the first draw and a queen on the second and (2) a queen on the first draw and a jack on the second. Thus we have two mutually exclusive events, and each one is broken into the *independent* events of first draw and second draw with replacement. Therefore the probability can be computed as follows:

$$\left(\frac{4}{52}\right)\left(\frac{4}{52}\right) + \left(\frac{4}{52}\right)\left(\frac{4}{52}\right) = \frac{32}{2704} = \frac{2}{169}$$

Jack on first draw; Queen on second draw; Queen on first draw; Jack on second draw ■

Problem Set 15.5

For Problems 1–22, solve each problem.

1. A die is tossed. Find the probability that a 5 came up if it is known that an odd number came up.

2. A die is tossed. Find the probability that a prime number was obtained, given that an even number came up. Also find the probability that an even number came up, given that a prime number was obtained.

3. Two dice are rolled and someone indicates that the two numbers that come up are different. Find the probability that the sum of the two numbers is 6.

4. Two dice are rolled, and someone indicates that the two numbers that come up are identical. Find the probability that the sum of the two numbers is 8.

5. One card is randomly drawn from a deck of 52 playing cards. Find the probability that it is a jack, given that the card is a face card. (We are considering jacks, queens, and kings as face cards.)

6. One card is randomly drawn from a deck of 52 playing cards. Find the probability that it is a spade, given the fact that it is a black card.

7. A coin and a die are tossed. Find the probability of getting a 5 on the die, given that a head comes up on the coin.

8. A family has three children. Assume that each child is as likely to be a boy as it is to be a girl. Find the probability that the family has three girls if it is known that the family has at least one girl.

9. The probability that a student will enroll in a mathematics course is 0.7, the probability that he or she will enroll in a history course is 0.3, and the probability that he or she will enroll in both mathematics and history is 0.2. Find the probability that a student will enroll in mathematics, given that he or she is also enrolled in history. Also find the probability that a student will enroll in history, given that he or she is also enrolled in mathematics.

10. The following probability table contains data relative to car accidents and weather conditions on a holiday weekend.

	Rain (R)	No rain (R')	Total
Accident (A)	0.025	0.015	0.040
No accident (A')	0.400	0.560	0.960
Total	0.425	0.575	1.000

Find the probability that a person chosen at random from the survey was in an accident, given that it was raining. Also find the probability that a person was not in an accident, given that it was not raining.

11. One hundred people were surveyed, and one question pertained to their educational background. The responses to this question are given in the following table.

	Female (F)	Male (F')	Total
College degree (D)	30	20	50
No college degree (D')	15	35	50
Total	45	55	100

Find the probability that a person chosen at random from the survey has a college degree, given that the person is female. Also find the probability that a person chosen is male, given that the person has a college degree.

12. In a recent election there were 1000 eligible voters. They were asked to vote on two issues, A and B. The results were as follows: 200 people voted for A, 400 people voted for B, and 50 people voted for both A and B. If one person is chosen at random from the 100 eligible voters, find the probability that the person voted for A, given that he or she voted for B. Also find the probability that the person voted for B, given that he or she voted for A.

13. A small company has 100 employees; among them 75 are males, 7 are administrators, and 5 of the administrators are males. If a person is chosen at random from the employees, find the probability that the person is an administrator, given that he is male. Also find the probability that the person chosen is female, given that she is an administrator.

14. A survey claims that 80% of the households in a certain town have a high-definition TV, 10% have a microwave oven, and 2% have both a high-definition TV and a microwave oven. Find the probability that a randomly selected household will have a microwave oven, given that it has a high-definition TV.

15. Consider a family of three children. Let E be the event, *the first child is a boy*, and let F be the event, *the family has exactly one boy*. Are events E and F dependent or independent?

16. Roll a white die and a green die. Let E be the event, *roll a 2 on the white die*, and let F be the event, *roll a 4 on the green die*. Are E and F dependent or independent events?

17. Toss three coins. Let E be the event, *toss not more than one head*, and let F be the event, *toss at least one of each face*. Are E and F dependent or independent events?

18. A card is drawn at random from a standard deck of 52 playing cards. Let E be the event, *the card is a 2*, and let F be the event, *the card is a 2 or a 3*. Are the events E and F dependent or independent?

19. A coin is tossed four times. Find the probability of getting three heads and one tail.

20. A coin is tossed five times. Find the probability of getting four heads and one tail.

21. Toss a pair of dice three times. Find the probability that a double is obtained on all three tosses.

22. Toss a pair of dice three times. Find the probability that each toss will produce a sum of 4.

For Problems 23–26, suppose that two cards are drawn in succession *without replacement* from a deck of 52 playing cards. Find the probability of each of the following events:

23. Both cards are 4's.

24. One card is an ace and one card is a king.

25. One card is a spade and one card is a diamond.

26. Both cards are black.

For Problems 27–30, suppose that two cards are drawn in succession *with replacement* from a deck of 52 playing cards. Find the probability of each of the following events:

27. Both cards are spades.

28. One card is an ace and one card is a king.

29. One card is the ace of spades and one card is the king of spades.

30. Both cards are red.

For Problems 31 and 32, solve each problem.

31. A person holds three kings from a deck of 52 playing cards. If the person draws two cards without replacement from the 49 cards remaining in the deck, find the probability of drawing the fourth king.

32. A person removes two aces and a king from a deck of 52 playing cards and draws, without replacement, two more cards from the deck. Find the probability that the person will draw two aces, or two kings, or an ace and a king.

For Problems 33–36, a bag contains five red and four white marbles. Two marbles are drawn in succession *with replacement*. Find the probability of each of the following events:

33. Both marbles drawn are red.

34. Both marbles drawn are white.

35. The first marble is red and the second marble is white.

36. At least one marble is red.

For Problems 37–40, a bag contains five white, four red, and four blue marbles. Two marbles are drawn in succession *with replacement*. Find the probability of each of the following events:

37. Both marbles drawn are white.

38. Both marbles drawn are red.

39. One red and one blue marble are drawn.

40. One white and one blue marble are drawn.

For Problems 41–44, a bag contains one red and two white marbles. Two marbles are drawn in succession *without replacement*. Find the probability of each of the following events:

41. One marble drawn is red, and one marble drawn is white.

42. The first marble drawn is red and the second is white.

43. Both marbles drawn are white.

44. Both marbles drawn are red.

For Problems 45–48, a bag contains five red and 12 white marbles. Two marbles are drawn in succession *without replacement*. Find the probability of each of the following events:

45. Both marbles drawn are red.

46. Both marbles drawn are white.

47. One red and one white marble are drawn.

48. At least one marble drawn is red.

For Problems 49–52, a bag contains two red, three white, and four blue marbles. Two marbles are drawn in succession *without replacement*. Find the probability of each of the following events:

49. Both marbles drawn are white.

50. One marble drawn is white, and one is blue.

51. Both marbles drawn are blue.

52. At least one red marble is drawn.

For Problems 53–56, a bag contains five white, one blue, and three red marbles. Three marbles are drawn in succession *with replacement*. Find the probability of each of the following events:

53. All three marbles drawn are blue.

54. One marble of each color is drawn.

55. One white and two red marbles are drawn.

56. One blue and two white marbles are drawn.

For Problems 57–60, a bag contains four white, one red, and two blue marbles. Three marbles are drawn in succession *without replacement*. Find the probability of each of the following events:

57. All three marbles drawn are white.

58. One red and two blue marbles are drawn.

59. One marble of each color is drawn.

60. One white and two red marbles are drawn.

For Problems 61 and 62, solve each problem.

61. Two boxes with red and white marbles are shown here. A marble is drawn at random from Box 1, and then a second marble is drawn from Box 2. Find the probability that both marbles drawn are white. Find the probability that both marbles drawn are red. Find the probability that one red and one white marble are drawn.

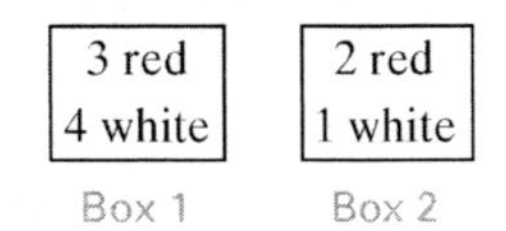

Box 1 Box 2

62. Three boxes containing red and white marbles are shown here. Randomly draw a marble from Box 1 and put it in Box 2. Then draw a marble from Box 2 and put it in Box 3. Then draw a marble from Box 3. What is the probability that the last marble drawn, from Box 3, is red? What is the probability that it is white?

Box 1	Box 2	Box 3
2 red 2 white	3 red 1 white	3 white

THOUGHTS INTO WORDS

63. How would you explain the concept of conditional probability to a classmate who missed the discussion of this section?

64. How would you give a nontechnical description of conditional probability to an elementary algebra student?

65. Explain in your own words the concept of independent events.

66. Suppose that a bag contains two red and three white marbles. Furthermore, suppose that two marbles are drawn from the bag in succession *with replacement*. Explain how the following tree diagram can be used to determine that the probability of drawing two white marbles is $\frac{9}{25}$.

First draw	Second draw	Outcomes
$\frac{2}{5}$ R	$\frac{2}{5}$ R	RR
	$\frac{3}{5}$ W	RW
$\frac{3}{5}$ W	$\frac{2}{5}$ R	WR
	$\frac{3}{5}$ W	WW

67. Explain how a tree diagram can be used to determine the probabilities for Problems 41–44.

15.6 Binomial Theorem

In Chapter 4, when multiplying polynomials, we developed patterns for squaring and cubing binomials. Now we want to develop a general pattern that can be used to raise a binomial to any positive integral power. Let's begin by looking at some specific expansions that can be verified by direct multiplication. (Note that the patterns for squaring and cubing a binomial are a part of this list.)

$$(x + y)^0 = 1$$

$$(x + y)^1 = x + y$$

$$(x + y)^2 = x^2 + 2xy + y^2$$

$$(x + y)^3 = x^3 + 3x^2y + 3xy^2 + y^3$$

$$(x + y)^4 = x^4 + 4x^3y + 6x^2y^2 + 4xy^3 + y^4$$

$$(x + y)^5 = x^5 + 5x^4y + 10x^3y^2 + 10x^2y^3 + 5xy^4 + y^5$$

First, note the pattern of the exponents for x and y on a term-by-term basis. The exponents of x begin with the exponent of the binomial and decrease by 1, term by term, until the last term has x^0, which is 1. The exponents of y begin with zero ($y^0 = 1$) and increase by 1, term by term, until the last term contains y to the power of the binomial. In other words, the variables in the expansion of $(x + y)^n$ have the following pattern.

$$x^n, \quad x^{n-1}y, \quad x^{n-2}y^2, \quad x^{n-3}y^3, \quad \ldots, \quad xy^{n-1}, \quad y^n$$

Note that for each term, the sum of the exponents of x and y is n.

Now let's look for a pattern for the coefficients by examining specifically the expansion of $(x + y)^5$.

$$(x + y)^5 = x^5 + 5x^4y^1 + 10x^3y^2 + 10x^2y^3 + 5x^1y^4 + 1y^5$$

$C(5, 1)$ $C(5, 2)$ $C(5, 3)$ $C(5, 4)$ $C(5, 5)$

As indicated by the arrows, the coefficients are numbers that arise as different-sized combinations of five things. To see why this happens, consider the coefficient for the term containing x^3y^2. The two y's (for y^2) come from two of the factors of $(x + y)$, and therefore the three x's (for x^3) must come from the other three factors of $(x + y)$. In other words, the coefficient is $C(5, 2)$.

We can now state a general expansion formula for $(x + y)^n$; this formula is often called the **binomial theorem**. But before stating it, let's make a small switch in notation. Instead of $C(n, r)$, we shall write $\binom{n}{r}$, which will prove to be a little more convenient at this time. The symbol $\binom{n}{r}$, still refers to the number of combinations of n things taken r at a time, but in this context it is often called a **binomial coefficient**.

Binomial Theorem

For any binomial $(x + y)$ and any natural number n,

$$(x + y)^n = x^n + \binom{n}{1}x^{n-1}y + \binom{n}{2}x^{n-2}y^2 + \cdots + \binom{n}{n}y^n$$

The binomial theorem can be proved by mathematical induction, but we will not do that in this text. Instead, we'll consider a few examples that put the binomial theorem to work.

EXAMPLE 1

Expand $(x + y)^7$.

Solution

$$(x + y)^7 = x^7 + \binom{7}{1}x^6y + \binom{7}{2}x^5y^2 + \binom{7}{3}x^4y^3 + \binom{7}{4}x^3y^4$$
$$+ \binom{7}{5}x^2y^5 + \binom{7}{6}xy^6 + \binom{7}{7}y^7$$
$$= x^7 + 7x^6y + 21x^5y^2 + 35x^4y^3 + 35x^3y^4 + 21x^2y^5 + 7xy^6 + y^7$$

■

EXAMPLE 2

Expand $(x - y)^5$.

Solution

We shall treat $(x - y)^5$ as $[x + (-y)]^5$.

$$[x + (-y)]^5 = x^5 + \binom{5}{1}x^4(-y) + \binom{5}{2}x^3(-y)^2 + \binom{5}{3}x^2(-y)^3$$
$$+ \binom{5}{4}x(-y)^4 + \binom{5}{5}(-y)^5$$
$$= x^5 - 5x^4y + 10x^3y^2 - 10x^2y^3 + 5xy^4 - y^5$$

■

EXAMPLE 3

Expand $(2a + 3b)^4$.

Solution

Let $x = 2a$ and $y = 3b$ in the binomial theorem.

$$(2a + 3b)^4 = (2a)^4 + \binom{4}{1}(2a)^3(3b) + \binom{4}{2}(2a)^2(3b)^2$$
$$+ \binom{4}{3}(2a)(3b)^3 + \binom{4}{4}(3b)^4$$
$$= 16a^4 + 96a^3b + 216a^2b^2 + 216ab^3 + 81b^4$$

■

EXAMPLE 4 Expand $\left(a + \frac{1}{n}\right)^5$.

Solution

$$\left(a + \frac{1}{n}\right)^5 = a^5 + \binom{5}{1}a^4\left(\frac{1}{n}\right) + \binom{5}{2}a^3\left(\frac{1}{n}\right)^2 + \binom{5}{3}a^2\left(\frac{1}{n}\right)^3 + \binom{5}{4}a\left(\frac{1}{n}\right)^4 + \binom{5}{5}\left(\frac{1}{n}\right)^5$$

$$= a^5 + \frac{5a^4}{n} + \frac{10a^3}{n^2} + \frac{10a^2}{n^3} + \frac{5a}{n^4} + \frac{1}{n^5}$$

■

EXAMPLE 5 Expand $(x^2 - 2y^3)^6$.

Solution

$$[x^2 + (-2y^3)]^6 = (x^2)^6 + \binom{6}{1}(x^2)^5(-2y^3) + \binom{6}{2}(x^2)^4(-2y^3)^2$$
$$+ \binom{6}{3}(x^2)^3(-2y^3)^3 + \binom{6}{4}(x^2)^2(-2y^3)^4$$
$$+ \binom{6}{5}(x^2)(-2y^3)^5 + \binom{6}{6}(-2y^3)^6$$
$$= x^{12} - 12x^{10}y^3 + 60x^8y^6 - 160x^6y^9 + 240x^4y^{12} - 192x^2y^{15} + 64y^{18}$$

■

Finding Specific Terms

Sometimes it is convenient to be able to write down the specific term of a binomial expansion without writing out the entire expansion. For example, suppose that we want the sixth term of the expansion $(x + y)^{12}$. We can proceed as follows: The sixth term will contain y^5. (Note in the binomial theorem that the **exponent of y is always one less than the number of the term.**) Because the sum of the exponents for x and y must be 12 (the exponent of the binomial), the sixth term will also contain x^7. The coefficient is $\binom{12}{5}$, where the 5 agrees with the exponent of y^5. Therefore the sixth term of $(x + y)^{12}$ is

$$\binom{12}{5}x^7y^5 = 792x^7y^5$$

EXAMPLE 6 Find the fourth term of $(3a + 2b)^7$.

Solution

The fourth term will contain $(2b)^3$, and therefore it will also contain $(3a)^4$. The coefficient is $\binom{7}{3}$. Thus the fourth term is

$$\binom{7}{3}(3a)^4(2b)^3 = (35)(81a^4)(8b^3) = 22{,}680a^4b^3$$

■

EXAMPLE 7 Find the sixth term of $(4x - y)^9$.

Solution

The sixth term will contain $(-y)^5$, and therefore it will also contain $(4x)^4$. The coefficient is $\binom{9}{5}$. Thus the sixth term is

$$\binom{9}{5}(4x)^4(-y)^5 = (126)(256x^4)(-y^5) = -32{,}256x^4y^5$$

■

Problem Set 15.6

For Problems 1–26, expand and simplify each binomial.

1. $(x + y)^8$

2. $(x + y)^9$

3. $(x - y)^6$

4. $(x - y)^4$

5. $(a + 2b)^4$

6. $(3a + b)^4$

7. $(x - 3y)^5$

8. $(2x - y)^6$

9. $(2a - 3b)^4$

10. $(3a - 2b)^5$

11. $(x^2 + y)^5$

12. $(x + y^3)^6$

13. $(2x^2 - y^2)^4$

14. $(3x^2 - 2y^2)^5$

15. $(x + 3)^6$

16. $(x + 2)^7$

17. $(x - 1)^9$

18. $(x - 3)^4$

19. $\left(1 + \frac{1}{n}\right)^4$

20. $\left(2 + \frac{1}{n}\right)^5$

21. $\left(a - \frac{1}{n}\right)^6$

22. $\left(2a - \frac{1}{n}\right)^5$

23. $(1 + \sqrt{2})^4$

24. $(2 + \sqrt{3})^3$

25. $(3 - \sqrt{2})^5$

26. $(1 - \sqrt{3})^4$

For Problems 27–36, write the first four terms of each expansion.

27. $(x + y)^{12}$

28. $(x + y)^{15}$

29. $(x - y)^{20}$

30. $(a - 2b)^{13}$

31. $(x^2 - 2y^3)^{14}$

32. $(x^3 - 3y^2)^{11}$

33. $\left(a + \frac{1}{n}\right)^9$

34. $\left(2 - \frac{1}{n}\right)^6$

35. $(-x + 2y)^{10}$

36. $(-a - b)^{14}$

For Problems 37–46, find the specified term for each binomial expansion.

37. The fourth term of $(x + y)^8$

38. The seventh term of $(x + y)^{11}$

39. The fifth term of $(x - y)^9$

40. The fourth term of $(x - 2y)^6$

41. The sixth term of $(3a + b)^7$

42. The third term of $(2x - 5y)^5$

43. The eighth term of $(x^2 + y^3)^{10}$

44. The ninth term of $(a + b^3)^{12}$

45. The seventh term of $\left(1 - \frac{1}{n}\right)^{15}$

46. The eighth term of $\left(1 - \frac{1}{n}\right)^{13}$

THOUGHTS INTO WORDS

47. How would you explain binomial expansions to an elementary algebra student?

48. Explain how to find the fifth term of the expansion of $(2x + 3y)^9$ without writing out the entire expansion.

49. Is the tenth term of the expansion $(1 - 2)^{15}$ positive or negative? Explain how you determined the answer to this question.

FURTHER INVESTIGATIONS

For Problems 50–53, expand and simplify each complex number.

50. $(1 + 2i)^5$

51. $(2 + i)^6$

52. $(2 - i)^6$

53. $(3 - 2i)^5$

Chapter 15 Summary

We can summarize this chapter with three main topics: counting techniques, probability, and the binomial theorem.

(15.1) Counting Techniques

The **fundamental principle of counting** states that if a first task can be accomplished in x ways and, following this task, a second task can be accomplished in y ways, then task 1 followed by task 2 can be accomplished in $x \cdot y$ ways. The principle extends to any finite number of tasks. As you solve problems involving the fundamental principle of counting, it is often helpful to analyze the problem in terms of the tasks to be completed.

(15.2) Ordered arrangements are called **permutations**. The number of permutations of n things taken n at a time is given by

$$P(n, n) = n!$$

The number of r-element permutations that can be formed from a set of n elements is given by

$$P(n, r) = \underbrace{n(n-1)(n-2)\cdots}_{r \text{ factors}}$$

If there are n elements to be arranged, where there are r_1 of one kind, r_2 of another kind, r_3 of another kind, . . . , r_k of a kth kind, then the number of distinguishable permutations is given by

$$\frac{n!}{(r_1!)(r_2!)(r_3!)\ldots(r_k!)}$$

Combinations are subsets; the order in which the elements appear does not make a difference. The number of r-element combinations (subsets) that can be formed from a set of n elements is given by

$$C(n, r) = \frac{P(n, r)}{r!}$$

Does the order in which the elements appear make any difference? This is a key question to consider when trying to decide whether a particular problem involves permutations or combinations. If the answer to the question is yes, then it is a permutation problem; if the answer is no, then it is a combination problem. Don't forget that combinations are subsets.

(15.3–15.5) Probability

In an experiment where all possible outcomes in the sample space S are equally likely to occur, the **probability** of an event E is defined by

$$P(E) = \frac{n(E)}{n(S)}$$

where $n(E)$ denotes the number of elements in the event E, and $n(S)$ denotes the number of elements in the sample space S. The numbers $n(E)$ and $n(S)$ can often be determined by using one or more of the previously listed counting techniques. For all events E, it is always true that $0 \leq P(E) \leq 1$. That is, all probabilities fall in the range from 0 to 1, inclusive.

If E and E' are **complementary events**, then $P(E) + P(E') = 1$. Therefore, if we can calculate either $P(E)$ or $P(E')$, then we can find the other one by subtracting from 1.

For two events E and F, the probability of E or F is given by

$$P(E \cup F) = P(E) + P(F) - P(E \cap F)$$

If $E \cap F = \varnothing$, then E and F are **mutually exclusive events**.

The probability that an event E occurs, given that another event F has already occurred, is called **conditional probability**. It is given by the equation

$$P(E|F) = \frac{P(E \cap F)}{P(F)}$$

Two events E and F are said to be **independent** if and only if

$$P(E \cap F) = P(E)P(F)$$

Two events that are not independent are called **dependent events**, and the probability of two dependent events is given by

$$P(E \cap F) = P(E)P(F|E)$$

(15.6) The Binomial Theorem

For any binomial $(x + y)$ and any natural number n,

$$(x + y)^n = x^n + \binom{n}{1}x^{n-1}y + \binom{n}{2}x^{n-2}y^2 + \cdots + \binom{n}{n}y^n$$

Note the following patterns in a binomial expansion:

1. In each term, the sum of the exponents of x and y is n.
2. The exponents of x begin with the exponent of the binomial and decrease by 1, term by term, until the last term has x^0, which is 1. The exponents of y begin with zero ($y^0 = 1$) and increase by 1, term by term, until the last term contains y to the power of the binomial.
3. The coefficient of any term is given by $\binom{n}{r}$, where the value of r agrees with the exponent of y for that term. For example, if the term contains y^3, then the coefficient of that term is $\binom{n}{3}$.
4. The expansion of $(x + y)^n$ contains $n + 1$ terms.

Chapter 15 Review Problem Set

Problems 1–14 are counting type problems.

1. How many different arrangements of the letters A, B, C, D, E, and F can be made?
2. How many different nine-letter arrangements can be formed from the nine letters of the word APPARATUS?
3. How many odd numbers of three different digits each can be formed by choosing from the digits 1, 2, 3, 5, 7, 8, and 9?
4. In how many ways can Arlene, Brent, Carlos, Dave, Ernie, Frank, and Gladys be seated in a row of seven seats so that Arlene and Carlos are side by side?
5. In how many ways can a committee of three people be chosen from six people?
6. How many committees consisting of three men and two women can be formed from seven men and six women?
7. How many different five-card hands consisting of all hearts can be formed from a deck of 52 playing cards?
8. If no number contains repeated digits, how many numbers greater than 500 can be formed by choosing from the digits 2, 3, 4, 5, and 6?
9. How many three-person committees can be formed from four men and five women so that each committee contains at least one man?
10. How many different four-person committees can be formed from eight people if two particular people refuse to serve together on a committee?
11. How many four-element subsets containing A or B but not both A and B can be formed from the set {A, B, C, D, E, F, G, H}?
12. How many different six-letter permutations can be formed from four identical H's and two identical T's?
13. How many four-person committees consisting of two seniors, one sophomore, and one junior can be formed from three seniors, four juniors, and five sophomores?
14. In a baseball league of six teams, how many games are needed to complete a schedule if each team plays eight games with each other team?

Problems 15–35 pose some probability questions.

15. If three coins are tossed, find the probability of getting two heads and one tail.
16. If five coins are tossed, find the probability of getting three heads and two tails.
17. What is the probability of getting a sum of 8 with one roll of a pair of dice?
18. What is the probability of getting a sum greater than 5 with one roll of a pair of dice?

19. Aimée, Brenda, Chuck, Dave, and Eli are randomly seated in a row of five seats. Find the probability that Aimée and Chuck are not seated side by side.

20. Four girls and three boys are to be randomly seated in a row of seven seats. Find the probability that the girls and boys will be seated in alternating seats.

21. Six coins are tossed. Find the probability of getting at least two heads.

22. Two cards are randomly chosen from a deck of 52 playing cards. What is the probability that two jacks are drawn?

23. Each arrangement of the six letters of the word CYCLIC is put on a slip of paper and placed in a hat. One slip is drawn at random. Find the probability that the slip contains an arrangement with the Y at the beginning.

24. A committee of three is randomly chosen from one man and six women. What is the probability that the man is not on the committee?

25. A four-person committee is selected at random from the eight people Alice, Bob, Carl, Dee, Enrique, Fred, Gina, and Hilda. Find the probability that Alice or Bob, but not both, is on the committee.

26. A committee of three is chosen at random from a group of five men and four women. Find the probability that the committee contains two men and one woman.

27. A committee of four is chosen at random from a group of six men and seven women. Find the probability that the committee contains at least one woman.

28. A bag contains five red and eight white marbles. Two marbles are drawn in succession *with replacement*. What is the probability that at least one red marble is drawn?

29. A bag contains four red, five white, and three blue marbles. Two marbles are drawn in succession *with replacement*. Find the probability that one red and one blue marble are drawn.

30. A bag contains four red and seven blue marbles. Two marbles are drawn in succession *without replacement*. Find the probability of drawing one red and one blue marble.

31. A bag contains three red, two white, and two blue marbles. Two marbles are drawn in succession *without replacement*. Find the probability of drawing at least one red marble.

32. Each of three letters is to be mailed in any one of four different mailboxes. What is the probability that all three letters will be mailed in the same mailbox?

33. The probability that a customer in a department store will buy a blouse is 0.15, the probability that she will buy a pair of shoes is 0.10, and the probability that she will buy both a blouse and a pair of shoes is 0.05. Find the probability that the customer will buy a blouse, given that she has already purchased a pair of shoes. Also find the probability that she will buy a pair of shoes, given that she has already purchased a blouse.

34. A survey of 500 employees of a company produced the following information.

Employment level	College degree	No college degree
Managerial	45	5
Nonmanagerial	50	400

Find the probability that an employee chosen at random (a) is working in a managerial position, given that he or she has a college degree; and (b) has a college degree, given that he or she is working in a managerial position.

35. From a survey of 1000 college students, it was found that 450 of them owned cars, 700 of them owned sound systems, and 200 of them owned both a car and a sound system. If a student is chosen at random from the 1000 students, find the probability that the student (a) owns a car, given the fact that he or she owns a sound system, and (b) owns a sound system, given the fact that he or she owns a car.

For Problems 36–41, expand each binomial and simplify.

36. $(x + 2y)^5$ **37.** $(x - y)^8$ **38.** $(a^2 - 3b^3)^4$

39. $\left(x + \frac{1}{n}\right)^6$ **40.** $(1 - \sqrt{2})^5$ **41.** $(-a + b)^3$

42. Find the fourth term of the expansion of $(x - 2y)^{12}$.

43. Find the tenth term of the expansion of $(3a + b^2)^{13}$.

Chapter 15 Test

For Problems 1–21, solve each problem.

1. In how many ways can Abdul, Barb, Corazon, and Doug be seated in a row of four seats so that Abdul occupies an end seat?

2. How many even numbers of four different digits each can be formed by choosing from the digits 1, 2, 3, 5, 7, 8, and 9?

3. In how many ways can three letters be mailed in six mailboxes?

4. In a baseball league of ten teams, how many games are needed to complete the schedule if each team plays six games against each other team?

5. In how many ways can a sum greater than 5 be obtained when tossing a pair of dice?

6. In how many ways can six different mathematics books and three different biology books be placed on a shelf so that all of the books in a subject area are side by side?

7. How many four-element subsets containing A or B, but not both A and B, can be formed from the set {A, B, C, D, E, F, G}?

8. How many five-card hands consisting of two aces, two kings, and one queen can be dealt from a deck of 52 playing cards?

9. How many different nine-letter arrangements can be formed from the nine letters of the word SASSAFRAS?

10. How many committees consisting of four men and three women can be formed from a group of seven men and five women?

11. What is the probability of rolling a sum less than 9 with a pair of dice?

12. Six coins are tossed. Find the probability of getting three heads and three tails.

13. All possible numbers of three different digits each are formed from the digits 1, 2, 3, 4, 5, and 6. If one number is then chosen at random, find the probability that it is greater than 200.

14. A four-person committee is selected at random from Anwar, Barb, Chad, Dick, Edna, Fern, and Giraldo. What is the probability that neither Anwar nor Barb is on the committee?

15. From a group of three men and five women, a three-person committee is selected at random. Find the probability that the committee contains at least one man.

16. A box of 12 items is known to contain one defective and 11 nondefective items. If a sample of three items is selected at random, what is the probability that all three items are nondefective?

17. Five coins are tossed 80 times. How many times should you expect to get three heads and two tails?

18. Suppose 3000 tickets are sold in a lottery. There are three prizes: The first prize is \$500, the second is \$300, and the third is \$100. What is the mathematical expectation of winning?

19. A bag contains seven white and 12 green marbles. Two marbles are drawn in succession, *with replacement.* Find the probability that one marble of each color is drawn.

20. A bag contains three white, five green, and seven blue marbles. Two marbles are drawn *without replacement.* Find the probability that two green marbles are drawn.

21. In an election there were 2000 eligible voters. They were asked to vote on two issues, A and B. The results were as follows: 500 people voted for A, 800 people voted for B, and 250 people voted for both A and B. If one person is chosen at random from the 2000 eligible voters, find the probability that this person voted for A, given that he or she voted for B.

22. Expand and simplify $\left(2 - \frac{1}{n}\right)^6$.

23. Expand and simplify $(3x + 2y)^5$.

24. Find the ninth term of the expansion of $\left(x - \frac{1}{2}\right)^{12}$.

25. Find the fifth term of the expansion of $(x + 3y)^7$.

CHAPTER 14

Problem Set 14.1 (page 741)

1. −4, −1, 2, 5, 8 **3.** 2, 0, −2, −4, −6 **5.** 2, 11, 26, 47, 74 **7.** 0, 2, 6, 12, 20 **9.** 4, 8, 16, 32, 64 **11.** $a_{15} = -79$; $a_{30} = -154$ **13.** $a_{25} = 1$; $a_{50} = -1$ **15.** $2n + 9$ **17.** $-3n + 5$ **19.** $\frac{n+2}{2}$ **21.** $4n - 2$ **23.** $-3n$ **25.** 73 **27.** 334 **29.** 35 **31.** 7 **33.** 86 **35.** 2700 **37.** 3200 **39.** −7950 **41.** 637.5 **43.** 4950 **45.** 1850 **47.** −2030 **49.** 3591 **51.** 40,000 **53.** 58,250 **55.** 2205 **57.** −1325 **59.** 5265 **61.** −810 **63.** 1276 **65.** 660 **67.** 55 **69.** 431 **75.** 3, 3, 7, 7, 11, 11 **77.** 4, 7, 10, 13, 17, 21 **79.** 4, 12, 36, 108, 324, 972 **81.** 1, 1, 2, 3, 5, 8 **83.** 3, 1, 4, 9, 25, 256

Problem Set 14.2 (page 750)

1. $3(2)^{n-1}$ **3.** 3^n **5.** $\left(\frac{1}{2}\right)^{n+1}$ **7.** 4^n **9.** $(0.3)^{n-1}$ **11.** $(-2)^{n-1}$ **13.** 64 **15.** $\frac{1}{9}$ **17.** −512 **19.** $\frac{1}{4374}$ **21.** $\frac{2}{3}$ **23.** 2 **25.** 1023 **27.** 19,682 **29.** $394\frac{1}{16}$ **31.** 1364 **33.** 1089 **35.** $7\frac{511}{512}$ **37.** −547 **39.** $127\frac{3}{4}$ **41.** 540 **43.** $2\frac{61}{64}$ **45.** 4 **47.** 3 **49.** No sum **51.** $\frac{27}{4}$ **53.** 2 **55.** $\frac{16}{3}$ **57.** $\frac{1}{3}$ **59.** $\frac{26}{99}$ **61.** $\frac{41}{333}$ **63.** $\frac{4}{15}$ **65.** $\frac{106}{495}$ **67.** $\frac{7}{3}$

Problem Set 14.3 (page 756)

1. \$24,200 **3.** 11,550 **5.** 7320 **7.** 125 liters **9.** 512 gallons **11.** \$116.25 **13.** \$163.84; \$327.67 **15.** \$24,900 **17.** 1936 feet **19.** $\frac{15}{16}$ of a gram **21.** 2910 feet **23.** 325 logs **25.** 5.9% **27.** $\frac{5}{64}$ of a gallon

Problem Set 14.4 (page 763)

These problems call for proof by mathematical induction and require class discussion.

Chapter 14 Review Problem Set (page 765)

1. $6n - 3$ **2.** 3^{n-2} **3.** $5(2^n)$ **4.** $-3n + 8$ **5.** $2n - 7$ **6.** 3^{3-n} **7.** $-(-2)^{n-1}$ **8.** $3n + 9$ **9.** $\frac{n+1}{3}$ **10.** 4^{n-1} **11.** 73 **12.** 106 **13.** $\frac{1}{32}$ **14.** $\frac{4}{9}$ **15.** −92 **16.** $\frac{1}{16}$ **17.** −5 **18.** 85 **19.** $\frac{5}{9}$ **20.** 2 or −2 **21.** $121\frac{40}{81}$ **22.** 7035 **23.** −10,725 **24.** $31\frac{31}{32}$ **25.** 32,015 **26.** 4757 **27.** $85\frac{21}{64}$ **28.** 37,044 **29.** 12,726 **30.** −1845 **31.** 225 **32.** 255 **33.** 8244 **34.** $85\frac{1}{3}$ **35.** $\frac{4}{11}$ **36.** $\frac{41}{90}$ **37.** \$750 **38.** \$46.50 **39.** \$3276.70 **40.** 10,935 gallons

Chapter 14 Test (page 767)

1. −226 **2.** 48 **3.** $-5n + 2$ **4.** $5(2)^{1-n}$ **5.** $6n + 4$ **6.** $\frac{729}{8}$ or $91\frac{1}{8}$ **7.** 223 **8.** 60 terms **9.** 2380 **10.** 765 **11.** 7155 **12.** 6138 **13.** 22,650 **14.** 9384 **15.** 4075 **16.** −341 **17.** 6 **18.** $\frac{1}{3}$ **19.** $\frac{2}{11}$ **20.** $\frac{4}{15}$ **21.** 3 liters **22.** \$1638.30 **23.** \$5810 **24.** and **25.** Instructor supplies proof.

CHAPTER 15

Problem Set 15.1 (page 773)

1. 20 **3.** 24 **5.** 168 **7.** 48 **9.** 36 **11.** 6840 **13.** 720 **15.** 720 **17.** 36 **19.** 24 **21.** 243 **23.** Impossible **25.** 216 **27.** 26 **29.** 36 **31.** 144 **33.** 1024 **35.** 30 **37.** **(a)** 6,084,000 **(c)** 3,066,336

Problem Set 15.2 (page 781)

1. 60 **3.** 360 **5.** 21 **7.** 252 **9.** 105 **11.** 1 **13.** 24 **15.** 84 **17.** **(a)** 336 **19.** 2880 **21.** 2450 **23.** 10 **25.** 10 **27.** 35 **29.** 1260 **31.** 2520 **33.** 15 **35.** 126 **37.** 144; 202 **39.** 15; 20 **41.** 20 **43.** 10; 15; 21; $\frac{n(n-1)}{2}$ **47.** 120 **53.** 133,784,560 **55.** 54,627,300

Problem Set 15.3 (page 788)

1. $\frac{1}{2}$ **3.** $\frac{3}{4}$ **5.** $\frac{1}{8}$ **7.** $\frac{7}{8}$ **9.** $\frac{1}{16}$ **11.** $\frac{3}{8}$ **13.** $\frac{1}{3}$ **15.** $\frac{1}{2}$ **17.** $\frac{5}{36}$ **19.** $\frac{1}{6}$ **21.** $\frac{11}{36}$ **23.** $\frac{1}{4}$ **25.** $\frac{1}{2}$ **27.** $\frac{1}{25}$ **29.** $\frac{9}{25}$ **31.** $\frac{2}{5}$ **33.** $\frac{9}{10}$ **35.** $\frac{5}{14}$ **37.** $\frac{15}{28}$ **39.** $\frac{7}{15}$ **41.** $\frac{1}{15}$ **43.** $\frac{2}{3}$

45. $\frac{1}{5}$ **47.** $\frac{1}{63}$ **49.** $\frac{1}{2}$ **51.** $\frac{5}{11}$ **53.** $\frac{1}{6}$ **55.** $\frac{21}{128}$ **57.** $\frac{13}{16}$
59. $\frac{1}{21}$ **63.** 40 **65.** 3744 **67.** 10,200 **69.** 123,552
71. 1,302,540

Problem Set 15.4 (page 797)

1. $\frac{5}{36}$ **3.** $\frac{7}{12}$ **5.** $\frac{1}{216}$ **7.** $\frac{53}{54}$ **9.** $\frac{1}{16}$ **11.** $\frac{15}{16}$ **13.** $\frac{1}{32}$
15. $\frac{31}{32}$ **17.** $\frac{5}{6}$ **19.** $\frac{12}{13}$ **21.** $\frac{7}{12}$ **23.** $\frac{37}{44}$ **25.** $\frac{2}{3}$ **27.** $\frac{2}{3}$
29. $\frac{5}{18}$ **31.** $\frac{1}{3}$ **33.** $\frac{1}{2}$ **35.** $\frac{7}{12}$ **37. (a)** 0.410 **(c)** 0.955
39. 0.525 **41.** 60 **43.** 120 **45.** 9 **47.** 56
49. It is a fair game. **51.** Yes **53.** \$11,000 **55.** −\$25
59. 1 to 7 **61.** 11 to 5 **63.** 1 to 8 **65.** 1 to 1 **67.** 4 to 3
69. 3 to 2 **71.** $\frac{2}{7}$ **73.** $\frac{7}{12}$

Problem Set 15.5 (page 806)

1. $\frac{1}{3}$ **3.** $\frac{2}{15}$ **5.** $\frac{1}{3}$ **7.** $\frac{1}{6}$ **9.** $\frac{2}{3}; \frac{2}{7}$ **11.** $\frac{2}{3}; \frac{2}{5}$ **13.** $\frac{1}{5}; \frac{2}{7}$
15. Dependent **17.** Independent **19.** $\frac{1}{4}$ **21.** $\frac{1}{216}$
23. $\frac{1}{221}$ **25.** $\frac{13}{102}$ **27.** $\frac{1}{16}$ **29.** $\frac{1}{1352}$ **31.** $\frac{2}{49}$ **33.** $\frac{25}{81}$
35. $\frac{20}{81}$ **37.** $\frac{25}{169}$ **39.** $\frac{32}{169}$ **41.** $\frac{2}{3}$ **43.** $\frac{1}{3}$ **45.** $\frac{5}{68}$
47. $\frac{15}{34}$ **49.** $\frac{1}{12}$ **51.** $\frac{1}{6}$ **53.** $\frac{1}{729}$ **55.** $\frac{5}{27}$ **57.** $\frac{4}{35}$
59. $\frac{8}{35}$ **61.** $\frac{4}{21}; \frac{2}{7}; \frac{11}{21}$

Problem Set 15.6 (page 813)

1. $x^8 + 8x^7y + 28x^6y^2 + 56x^5y^3 + 70x^4y^4 + 56x^3y^5 + 28x^2y^6 + 8xy^7 + y^8$
3. $x^6 - 6x^5y + 15x^4y^2 - 20x^3y^3 + 15x^2y^4 - 6xy^5 + y^6$
5. $a^4 + 8a^3b + 24a^2b^2 + 32ab^3 + 16b^4$
7. $x^5 - 15x^4y + 90x^3y^2 - 270x^2y^3 + 405xy^4 - 243y^5$
9. $16a^4 - 96a^3b + 216a^2b^2 - 216ab^3 + 81b^4$
11. $x^{10} + 5x^8y + 10x^6y^2 + 10x^4y^3 + 5x^2y^4 + y^5$
13. $16x^8 - 32x^6y^2 + 24x^4y^4 - 8x^2y^6 + y^8$
15. $x^6 + 18x^5 + 135x^4 + 540x^3 + 1215x^2 + 1458x + 729$
17. $x^9 - 9x^8 + 36x^7 - 84x^6 + 126x^5 - 126x^4 + 84x^3 - 36x^2 + 9x - 1$
19. $1 + \frac{4}{n} + \frac{6}{n^2} + \frac{4}{n^3} + \frac{1}{n^4}$
21. $a^6 - \frac{6a^5}{n} + \frac{15a^4}{n^2} - \frac{20a^3}{n^3} + \frac{15a^2}{n^4} - \frac{6a}{n^5} + \frac{1}{n^6}$
23. $17 + 12\sqrt{2}$ **25.** $843 - 589\sqrt{2}$
27. $x^{12} + 12x^{11}y + 66x^{10}y^2 + 220x^9y^3$
29. $x^{20} - 20x^{19}y + 190x^{18}y^2 - 1140x^{17}y^3$
31. $x^{28} - 28x^{26}y^3 + 364x^{24}y^6 - 2912x^{22}y^9$
33. $a^9 + \frac{9a^8}{n} + \frac{36a^7}{n^2} + \frac{84a^6}{n^3}$
35. $x^{10} - 20x^9y + 180x^8y^2 - 960x^7y^3$ **37.** $56x^5y^3$
39. $126x^5y^4$ **41.** $189a^2b^5$ **43.** $120x^6y^{21}$ **45.** $\frac{5005}{n^6}$
51. $-117 + 44i$ **53.** $-597 - 122i$

Chapter 15 Review Problem Set (page 816)

1. 720 **2.** 30,240 **3.** 150 **4.** 1440 **5.** 20 **6.** 525
7. 1287 **8.** 264 **9.** 74 **10.** 55 **11.** 40 **12.** 15
13. 60 **14.** 120 **15.** $\frac{3}{8}$ **16.** $\frac{5}{16}$ **17.** $\frac{5}{36}$ **18.** $\frac{13}{18}$ **19.** $\frac{3}{5}$
20. $\frac{1}{35}$ **21.** $\frac{57}{64}$ **22.** $\frac{1}{221}$ **23.** $\frac{1}{6}$ **24.** $\frac{4}{7}$ **25.** $\frac{4}{7}$
26. $\frac{10}{21}$ **27.** $\frac{140}{143}$ **28.** $\frac{105}{169}$ **29.** $\frac{1}{6}$ **30.** $\frac{28}{55}$ **31.** $\frac{5}{7}$
32. $\frac{1}{16}$ **33.** $\frac{1}{2}; \frac{1}{3}$ **34. (a)** $\frac{9}{19}$ **(b)** $\frac{9}{10}$ **35. (a)** $\frac{2}{7}$
(b) $\frac{4}{9}$ **36.** $x^5 + 10x^4y + 40x^3y^2 + 80x^2y^3 + 80xy^4 + 32y^5$
37. $x^8 - 8x^7y + 28x^6y^2 - 56x^5y^3 + 70x^4y^4 - 56x^3y^5 + 28x^2y^6 - 8xy^7 + y^8$
38. $a^8 - 12a^6b^3 + 54a^4b^6 - 108a^2b^9 + 81b^{12}$
39. $x^6 + \frac{6x^5}{n} + \frac{15x^4}{n^2} + \frac{20x^3}{n^3} + \frac{15x^2}{n^4} + \frac{6x}{n^5} + \frac{1}{n^6}$
40. $41 - 29\sqrt{2}$ **41.** $-a^3 + 3a^2b - 3ab^2 + b^3$
42. $-1760x^9y^3$ **43.** $57{,}915a^4b^{18}$

Chapter 15 Test (page 818)

1. 12 **2.** 240 **3.** 216 **4.** 270 **5.** 26 **6.** 8640 **7.** 20
8. 144 **9.** 2520 **10.** 350 **11.** $\frac{13}{18}$ **12.** $\frac{5}{16}$ **13.** $\frac{5}{6}$
14. $\frac{1}{7}$ **15.** $\frac{23}{28}$ **16.** $\frac{3}{4}$ **17.** 25 **18.** \$0.30 **19.** $\frac{168}{361}$
20. $\frac{2}{21}$ **21.** $\frac{5}{16}$
22. $64 - \frac{192}{n} + \frac{240}{n^2} - \frac{160}{n^3} + \frac{60}{n^4} - \frac{12}{n^5} + \frac{1}{n^6}$
23. $243x^5 + 810x^4y + 1080x^3y^2 + 720x^2y^3 + 240xy^4 + 32y^5$
24. $\frac{495}{256}x^4$ **25.** $2835x^3y^4$